The Dragon Slayer with a Heavy Heart

The Dragon Slayer with a Heavy Heart

A Powerful Story About Finding
Happiness and Serenity...

...Even When You Really, REALLY
Wish Some Things Were Different

MARCIA POWERS

MELVIN POWERS
WILSHIRE BOOK COMPANY

My deepest appreciation to Carole Foley for her dedication and ever-ready help during the preparation of this book for publication.

My heartfelt thanks to Melvin Powers for his ongoing support and his enthusiasm for my stories that teach principles of psychological growth.

MELVIN POWERS
WILSHIRE BOOK COMPANY
9731 Variel Avenue
Chatsworth, California 91311-4315
Web site: www.mpowers.com

Library of Congress Control Number 2003107882
ISBN 978-0-87980-450-3
Printed in the United States of America

For information regarding quantity discounts for bulk purchases, write to Wilshire Book Company Special Markets Division or e-mail mpowers@mpowers.com.

To Dr. Albert Ellis, my teacher and dear friend, whose internationally renowned philosophy and techniques have changed the face of psychology forever and lightened the hearts of people everywhere.

In memory of Dr. Reinhold Niebuhr, whose famous, insightful Serenity Prayer has circled the world and become a guiding light for millions.

Contents

ONE • The Dragon Slayer's Plight   1

TWO • An Unforgettable Mission   15

THREE • An Encounter with the Wise One   21

FOUR • Prescription for a Heavy Heart   28

FIVE • The Path of Serenity   39

SIX • Lessons for the Heart   49

SEVEN • A New Kind of Dragon-Slayer Bravery   61

EIGHT • The Land of Serenity   75

NINE • An Arresting Development   87

TEN • The Universe Versus Duke the Dragon Slayer   93

ELEVEN • The Battle of Acceptance County   102

TWELVE • The Mystery of the O Well   110

THIRTEEN • The Showdown   115

FOURTEEN • The Land of Courage   124

FIFTEEN • An Ordinary Hero   136

SIXTEEN • The Leap of Faith   142

SEVENTEEN • The Moment of Surrender   156

EIGHTEEN • The Bridge of Change   165

NINETEEN • Going Home   171

CHAPTER ONE

The Dragon Slayer's Plight

A long time ago in a land far away, there lived a famous dragon slayer named Duke. He was as fast as a bolt of lightning, as powerful as a tornado, and able to slay his prey with a single thrust of his sword. No wonder he was the number one dragon slayer in all the land, as his father and his father's father had been before him.

Duke was a familiar sight, racing through the cobblestone streets in his bright red dragon wagon pulled by a team of majestic white stallions. His trusty canine sidekick, Prince, sat next to him and barked excitedly at villagers to move aside. People waved and cheered as their fearless hero thundered by. Even when he was not on a mission, Duke always traveled in the dragon wagon, ready to roll immediately whenever summoned for an emergency.

He was a real born-and-bred hero, a man's man and a woman's dream. At least that's what the ladies always said . . . when they first met him.

Off duty, his favorite thing to do was to unwind at the Hero Shoppe, browsing through the latest in hero tools or hanging out at the shoppe's Juice Bar Station, swapping stories with his fellow heroes.

Sometimes on weekends he would bring his son to the shoppe. One Saturday afternoon they sat at the juice bar, drinking their usual Mega-fruit Specials and munching on Macho Mocha Squares while Duke's buddies told real-life stories about dragons they had slain, villagers they had protected, fires they had fought, and emergency treatment they had administered.

Duke leaned over to Jonathan. "Every time I bring you here, Johnny, it reminds me of how excited I was, sitting at this same juice bar with my father and grandfather, hearing great adventures just like the ones you're listening to now."

"I know, Father," Jonathan said, smiling uneasily. "But I have homework to do. Can we go now?"

"Uh, well, I guess so," Duke replied, disappointed at Jonathan's lack of enthusiasm.

On their way out Duke pointed to an empty space beside the grand portraits of himself, his father, and his grandfather that hung prominently side by side on the Heroes Wall of Fame. "Remember, Johnny, that's where *your* portrait will hang someday," he said proudly.

Jonathan nodded and continued toward the exit without looking up.

Duke sighed and glanced back at the portraits, recalling how eager he had been when his own father had pointed at the same wall and said the same thing to him.

My father's prophecy came true, Duke thought, *and so will mine!*

The next morning Duke sat at the breakfast table with his wife, reading the *Kingdom Times*. Feeling her eyes on him, he glanced up to see her gazing at him longingly.

"What is it, Allie?" he asked.

"I was just wondering . . ." she said quietly.

He looked back at the paper. "Wondering what?"

"Wondering how I can love you so much yet know you so little." Her voice quavered ever so slightly.

"Oh, Allie, not this again, please."

"But you never *talk* to me."

"How can you *say* that?" He set down the paper. "I talk to you all the time. I'm talking to you right now."

"I've told you. You don't talk to me about what really matters. Half the time when I try to tell you what's going on around here your mind's off in another world."

"What do you mean?" he asked, dismayed. "You are my world, Allie—you and Johnny. You know that."

"Sometimes it doesn't seem like it. I want us to be closer. I want to know the *real* Duke—the man you keep hidden inside a dragon-slaying suit."

"You know I've never been good at that kind of stuff." He flexed his biceps teasingly. "Come on, Allie, feel my muscles like you used to."

She lowered her head to hide the tears puddling up in her eyes. He reached out to take her in his arms, but she pushed him away. "You don't have to be strong *all* the time," she murmured.

"That's how I'm *supposed* to be. I'm a rough, tough dragon-slaying hero, remember?"

She sighed. "You're just like your father, always thinking you know the way things should be."

"So what's wrong with that? I never heard my mother complain. Besides, it's not like I've changed. I'm the same guy I've always been—the same guy you fell in love with. Come on, Allie, you know you wouldn't want me any other way."

Allie threw up her hands in frustration. "You just don't get it!" she shouted, springing from her chair and running from the room.

He jumped up and went after her. "No, I *don't* get it, Allie! I am who I am, and you shouldn't be trying to make me into someone I'm not. It isn't right!"

"If it isn't right, then why are you always trying to make Jonathan into someone *he's* not?" she cried out, slamming the bedroom door.

Duke sank into the nearest chair. "Women!" he said, exasperated. His father was right: It *is* easier to slay a dragon than to understand a woman.

The distance between Duke and Allie grew and grew until finally one day she said, "I'm as lonely when you're here as I am when you're not. I just can't take it anymore."

She told him to pack up his hero tools, his trophies and his awards—and especially his idea of how things should and should not be—take his dog, hop into his dragon wagon, and ride off to fight his way through life without her.

Duke was indignant. "But we're the perfect couple, Allie," he protested. "You *know* we are. *Everyone* thinks so!"

Allie stood firm.

Pain cut through him like a knife. Angrily he gathered his belongings and threw them into trunks that he shoved, one by one, into the dragon wagon. He hopped up onto the seat, whistled to Prince, and drove off. "It shouldn't *be* like this," he muttered. "It isn't fair! This is *awful*! It's *terrible*! She can't do this to me!"

Over the cobblestone streets and past the village square he muttered and rode and muttered some more, all the way to a furnished bachelor-pad rent-a-castle on the outskirts of town.

With Prince running in and out of the castle behind him, Duke reluctantly unloaded the wagon, all the while thinking about how Allie was messing up his life. Why was this happening? He had spent years protecting her from the danger and fear that were part of his daily life, and this was the thanks he got!

When he finished, he surveyed the anteroom filled with trunks containing his fine hero tools, his hard-won trophies and awards, and his other possessions all sitting on the floor of a castle they didn't belong in.

He shook his head. "This is a fine mess you got me into, Allie," he groused, unable to remember where he had heard that before. Then he started unpacking as Prince darted from room to room, sniffing here and sniffing there, getting acquainted with their new home.

Irritated that he had not taken the time to label the trunks, Duke raised the lid of the nearest one and looked inside. On top lay the purple velvet bag that held the special sword he had had made to give his son on his thirteenth birthday. He lifted the bag and pulled out the sword. Jonathan's initials were engraved on it just below the carved ivory handle, next to the family crest. Duke gazed at the weapon admiringly. It was a sword any dragon slayer would be proud to own.

As he thought of his son, his anger turned to sadness. He missed Jonathan already, even though being with him these days was often frustrating. It had become such an effort to get him to go to his fencing and javelin-throwing lessons. He wasn't enthusiastic about hanging out at the Hero Shoppe, either. *Why?* Duke wondered. *Any boy should be thrilled to do these things!*

With his stomach feeling like cream sloshing in a churn, Duke set the sword down and began pacing back and forth, talking to himself and cracking his knuckles. He did his best thinking while pacing and cracking.

Always ready for some extra exercise, Prince trailed back and forth behind him. Of course they couldn't do their best pacing because they had to go around so many trunks.

"I ought to be home where I belong," Duke grumbled, "teaching my son how to fulfill his destiny! How am I going to keep him on the right track if I don't even live in the same castle?"

He paced faster, his voice rising. "Someone has to get that reluctant dragon slayer–in–training to go to his lessons and to practice! What am I going to do?"

Suddenly Duke noticed a strange heaviness in his chest. He decided to ignore it, figuring that it would go away. But throughout the evening, as he unpacked—periodically stopping to pace, crack, and grumble some more—the heaviness grew worse.

When he awoke at dawn, his chest felt so heavy that he thought Prince was sitting on it, but his best buddy was sprawled beside him.

"Oh, great!" Duke said. "All I need now is to get sick. It's all Allie's fault! First she throws me out of my own castle, and now this!"

As it turned out, the dragon slayer didn't get sick, yet the heaviness he felt lingered on and on. He missed seeing his son get up in the morning and go to bed at night. And as angry as he was with Allie, he missed her too, and their castle, and their life together.

Moving on with his life wasn't going to be easy, but after a while he decided he had better try.

Before long Duke started dating Cindy, one of the eye-batting, hero-worshiping blond servers at the Juice Bar Station. The new romance lifted some of the heaviness from his chest.

Believing everything was going well, Duke was caught off guard when, after months of seeing each other, Cindy began insisting that he didn't talk to her, *really* talk to her, and that she was growing tired of trying to get through to him.

One warm summer evening the couple attended a Traveling Troubadours musical performance at Ye Olde Outdoor Theater in the village square.

At intermission Duke turned to Cindy. "You've hardly said a word since I picked you up, and every time I take your hand you pull it away. What's wrong?"

A pained look flashed across Cindy's face. "It's nothing."

"Come on, Cindy," he urged. "Tell me."

"This isn't the time or place," she said in a hushed voice. "I was planning to tell you later."

"I'm not going to spend the whole evening like this. Just tell me now."

The words Cindy had been holding back for some time came tumbling out. "I can't go on this way. I'm drinking more juice than I'm serving the customers. I want more than just a superhero to admire."

"I thought you liked big, strong, rough, tough heroes," Duke replied, flexing his biceps playfully.

"I do, but that's not enough."

He tried to put his arm around her, but she sighed and turned away. "You just don't understand."

A vague, familiar discomfort rose within him. "Listen, Cindy, I am who I am. You shouldn't try to make me be someone I'm not. It isn't right."

"Well, it isn't right for me to be as lonely when I'm with you as I am when I'm by myself, either. This is it, Duke the Dragon Slayer. We're through."

"But—"

"Nothing you can say will make me change my mind," she said emphatically. "And don't look for me at the Hero Shoppe anymore. I need a change of scenery. I'm going to Muscle Beach. I've heard it's the best place for a girl to wash away the blues."

She stood up, tucked her purse under her arm, and with a toss of her hair, marched out of his life.

When he returned home to the rent-a-castle, Duke stomped back and forth, cracking his knuckles, Cindy's words whirling around in his mind.

"I can't believe this!" he wailed. "It's not fair! How could this happen to me again? I should've known better than to trust another woman. I was stupid to get involved!"

Suddenly he heard Allie in his mind too, as clearly as if she were standing right there. He covered his ears, trying to shut out the women's voices. That didn't work, so he tried talking over them, but their voices only got louder. Soon all three of them were yelling.

"That's it!" he bellowed. "I've had it with women! They swoon over you, and then—*bam!*—they try to change you. First they want you one way, and then they want you another. You can't win! I'm never going through this again!"

He ranted and raved nonstop about Cindy and Allie until he was exhausted. When he fell into bed, his chest felt heavier than ever.

Day after day the heaviness in Duke's heart increased and his energy decreased. And day after day he became more annoyed with his condition. He tried ordering the heaviness to go away, but it refused to be intimidated.

The discomfort in his chest began waking him during the night, and he would lie in bed for hours wondering and worrying about it. Soon he couldn't drag himself through the day without taking an afternoon nap, which proved to be a problem whenever he was on a dragon-slaying mission. He started going to bed earlier, but that only gave him more time to worry.

Finally the dragon slayer decided he had better get some help. He sought out the royal physician.

"I can't stand this anymore!" Duke told him. "You have to find out what's wrong with me and give me one of your tonics to get rid of it!"

The physician examined him thoroughly. "You're in perfect health," he announced.

"You call *this* perfect health?" Duke snapped, pressing his fist to his chest.

"I wish I could help," the physician replied sympathetically, "but I know of no tonic that will cure what is weighing on your heart."

"My heart?"

The physician nodded. "I'm sorry, but this sort of problem is out of my area of expertise."

Panic grabbed Duke by the throat. "You're the best doctor in the kingdom! If you can't help me, who can?"

The physician thought for a moment. "Perhaps a specialist. I have heard talk of a Wise One who can solve even the most perplexing and troublesome problems. Perhaps he could provide an answer."

Duke's face brightened. "A specialist! That's it! Where can I find him?"

Unfortunately, the physician had no idea.

Duke asked around at the Hero Shoppe, and although many people had heard of the Wise One, some said he was only a myth—and no one knew where to find him.

Soon Jonathan's birthday came. Even though Duke hadn't been in a partying mood for some time, he had invited some of his son's friends and the regulars from the Hero Shoppe to a surprise celebration. He had ordered Jonathan's favorite birthday cake, double chocolate with peanut-butter filling.

After dinner the cake was brought in and held up for everyone to see. Duke proudly read aloud the words that were written on top in red icing: "Happy 13th Birthday Johnny, Future #1 Dragon Slayer."

The guests lifted their goblets. "To Johnny," a chorus of voices rang out. The boy fidgeted in his seat, playing nervously with the napkin in his lap.

Duke placed a long, narrow, brightly wrapped package on the table in front of his son. Jonathan methodically opened it, revealing a purple velvet bag. He loosened the drawstring and pulled out the distinctive sword that Duke had saved for this day.

It was an exact copy of Duke's own now famous lucky sword, made for him by his father and given to him long ago on his thirteenth birthday—a sword fashioned after his father's and grandfather's, which they were convinced had helped them battle their way to the top in the dragon-slaying business.

Oohs and *ahs* resounded throughout the room, and Duke's mind was flooded with memories of how proud and excited he had been when he received his sword.

"Johnny," he began, "this is truly a great moment in your—"

"I can't take this, Father," Jonathan interrupted, the sword in his outstretched hands. "I can't take *any* of this anymore!"

He pushed the sword into his father's hands.

Duke was stunned. Everyone shifted uncomfortably in their seats.

"I'm tired of going where I don't want to go and doing what I don't like to do," Jonathan blurted out. "I hate my javelin-throwing lessons. I'm no good at fencing. I'm always getting hurt. I like chess better than jousting, and I'd rather hear lectures at the Royal Academy than sit and listen to stories at the Hero Shoppe.

"I can't be what you want me to be, Father. I'm never

going to be a dragon slayer. I'm Jonathan, not Johnny." His lower lip began to quiver. "I'm sorry. I'm so sorry, Father, but I can't be you."

Then he bolted from the room.

Guests filed out as if they were leaving a funeral. Some stopped to shake Duke's trembling hand in sympathy; others patted him on the back. Almost everyone averted their eyes.

Duke found Jonathan sitting in the dragon wagon. He put the sword in the back and drove his son home. The only sounds were the grinding of the wooden wheels and the clopping of the horses' hooves on the cobblestone streets.

Duke's mind was racing. *This is awful! This is terrible! Never a dragon slayer indeed! My son must be what he was meant to be, what he was born to be. He'll have to change, that's all!* But Duke was too upset and too afraid of what he might say—what they both might say—to tell Jonathan right then.

After what seemed to be an endless ride, Duke stopped the dragon wagon in front of his old castle.

Jonathan looked at his father sadly. "Why can't you just like me the way I am, like Edward does?"

"Who is Edward?" Duke asked, feeling as if someone were about to stab him in the stomach.

"He's Mother's special friend. We met him one night when he was lecturing at the Royal Academy—never mind. I shouldn't have mentioned it."

While Duke struggled to reply, Jonathan climbed down from the wagon. "Goodnight, Father," he said softly, lowering his head. "I'm sorry. I didn't mean to ruin your surprise."

Then he turned and walked, shoulders slumped, to the castle door.

After he watched his son go inside, Duke reached over and stroked Prince. "What am I going to do, boy, huh?"

That night the heaviness in Duke's chest grew even worse. He felt as if his heart had a boulder inside it.

"This is your fault, Johnny," he said, pounding his fist to his chest. "And that's *Johnny*—not Jonathan! You'll never be a Jonathan if *I* have anything to say about it, no matter what this Edward person says. Do you hear me? How could you do this to me after all I've done for you? It isn't right! It isn't fair! I don't deserve this! I'm going to hound you until the day I die!"

Every day from then on, Duke looked in the mirror to see if he looked as heavy as he felt. Every day he looked sadder and more tired but no bigger.

As the days passed, his heart grew heavier and heavier with the weight of all that should be and all that should not be, with all that has to be and all that must not be, with all that is meant to be and all that is not meant to be, with all that is awful and terrible and all that he could not stand.

And as the heaviness grew, Duke's lightning-bolt speed began to wane. He could no longer sprint to the dragon wagon and vault onto the seat when summoned for a mission. His fancy jig-paced footwork, which he often used to dazzle the dragons before lunging in for the kill, now looked more like a waltz. Fortunately no one except Prince had witnessed this, and he could always be counted on to keep the dragon slayer's secrets. But Duke knew that if his slowdown continued, it was only a matter of time before his missions would be at risk and rumors would begin to circulate. *That* he could not let happen. He had to do something fast.

He tried putting ice compresses on his chest, figuring they might shrink his heavy heart. That was a complete waste of time, and it was a nuisance having to mop up the little puddles on the floor from the melting ice.

Next, Duke went to the Hero Shoppe and bought a light-weight chest guard, a face shield, and a pair of ultralight boots. That didn't work either, so he decided to go on a strict diet. *Maybe I can lose weight faster than my heart is gaining it,* he thought.

No such luck.

Duke was running out of options. He tried to drown his sorrows one night by getting juiced at the Hero Shoppe, but all that did was get him into such a state that he mistakenly went home to his old castle and got thrown out—again.

After a while his heart got so heavy that he had to lean back just to keep from falling forward. This posed quite a problem, especially when he was charging a dragon. Twice he nearly toppled over.

He tried wearing a backpack with rocks in it to offset the weight, but that was so cumbersome he could hardly move around. Duke knew all too well that in his business, being slow or off balance could mean disaster, but he didn't know what else to do. He had tried everything he could think of.

More and more, thoughts about his troubles cluttered his mind. Often he didn't even realize that he had stopped paying attention to what he was doing until it was too late. He kept bumping into things and was getting forgetful.

He feared he was losing his grip altogether when a pottery jug of apple cider slipped right through his fingers and crashed onto the stone floor, shattering into a thousand sticky, jagged pieces.

Prince raced in and skidded to a stop just before his paws slid into the slippery mess.

"Stay there, boy," Duke called out.

He bent down, pressing his hand against his leg to brace himself against the weight of his heart, and started picking up some of the larger pieces of pottery.

Suddenly he cut his hand on one of them. He groaned. "It figures."

He poured some spirits over the gash and tied a clean cloth around his hand, trying not to think about what else could go wrong. Not that it really mattered.

Nothing much mattered anymore.

CHAPTER TWO

An Unforgettable Mission

The next morning Duke was again pacing back and forth, cracking his knuckles and complaining to Prince. "I've heard of people having a heavy heart, but this is ridiculous! Allie and Cindy and Johnny are ruining my life!"

He was furious with them for causing the heaviness in his heart and was angry with himself for not being able to get rid of it. Sometimes he was even angry with himself for being angry.

"It's wrong! All wrong. Everything is wrong," he said. "Things shouldn't be this way. They should be the way they're supposed to be, the way they're meant to be, the way they used to be, the way they have to be. I can't stand this!"

Apparently tired of all the pacing he and Duke had been doing lately, Prince sat this one out. He didn't sit for long, though, as a pecking sound sent him to the window.

Duke smiled when he saw the carrier pigeon from the Premiere Emergency Messenger Service. He flung open the window. "*Hola! Hola*, Sebastian!"

The pigeon, a great lover of Latin music, danced around on one leg to a cha-cha beat—hop, hop, hop-hop-hop—and shook the other leg toward Duke. On it was an elastic band holding a rolled-up note. Of course the dragon slayer already knew that whenever Sebastian arrived it was to deliver a message, but Sebastian wouldn't be Sebastian without the dance.

"*Gracias*," Duke said. He removed the note, uneasy at the thought of an upcoming mission. He waved good-bye as the pigeon flew off.

He read the message and sighed. "Okay, boy, we have a dragon to slay. Let's go."

Prince ran to the back door. He barked and barked until Duke caught up, then raced outside and across the grounds to the barn, the dragon slayer plodding after him. The dog jumped up and down impatiently as Duke struggled to pull his fire-retardant dragon-slaying attire over his clothes. He changed his boots and hitched up the horses.

As he and Prince raced through the streets in the dragon wagon, Duke's heart was so heavy that it no longer pounded with excitement the way it used to. The waving, cheering villagers they passed didn't excite him either. He was just going mindlessly through the motions.

Ominous dark clouds gathering above matched his mood. *Can a gray mood make a gray day?* he wondered. He was glad he had his inclement-weather gear in the trunk of hero tools he kept in the wagon. One never knew when a super-duper, all-weather dragon-slaying suit with nonskid boots, tight-grip gloves, and face shield with rain diverter would come in handy.

By the time he and Prince reached the cave where the dragon had been sighted, a light rain had begun to fall. Their prey was nowhere in sight.

Too bad it isn't raining harder, Duke thought, recalling the many times he had used stormy weather to great advantage. Prince would sniff out the dragon, and Duke, surefooted and fast, would zip up behind it, the sound of his footsteps and the drawing of his sword swallowed up by the clapping thunder, whipping wind, and raindrops beating on the rocks and the ground. Often it would all be over in a matter of moments.

Although ambushing a dragon from behind was the safest technique, Duke usually preferred to challenge the beast head-on, man to dragon, and use his expert moves to win fair and square. It was a matter of honor—and of the thrill of the contest.

But today was different. Today Duke quivered at the thought of a face-to-face battle with a gigantic, powerful, fire-breathing beast. He assessed the situation carefully, as any good dragon slayer would. In his present state he couldn't move much faster than a cumbersome dragon and he would be a lot less steady on his feet. If ever there was a time when relying on the element of surprise was a good idea, this was the day. But catching the dragon unaware didn't seem likely unless the storm worsened soon—and he couldn't count on that. Besides, he suspected that the dragon was inside the cave, and getting behind it without being detected would be difficult. Duke knew there had to be a better way.

Then he got an idea.

He signaled Prince to go into the cave and lure the dragon out. Meanwhile he climbed onto some rocks above the mouth of the cave and waited.

When Prince came running out of the cave, the dragon came lumbering after him. Duke waited silently until the beast passed below him. Then he leaped to the ground a few feet behind the dragon. The moment he hit the ground a sharp pain shot through his ankle, and down he went onto the moist dirt. "Drat this extra weight!"

The dragon stopped, turned, and glared down at him. Duke had never seen a dragon from the ground before. It was huge. And it was so close he could see raindrops trickling down its shiny scales. The beast let out the deafening sound made by agitated dragons and shot streams of fire threateningly into the air.

Figuring he didn't have time to struggle to his feet and unsure whether he could stand on his injured ankle, Duke drew his prized sword and pointed it menacingly at the dragon. Neither impressed nor frightened, the dragon continued shooting streams of fire, this time at the ground, mere inches away from the dragon slayer.

Duke was grateful that his dragon-slaying suit was fire retardant, but his sword got so hot it burned his hand right through his tight-grip glove. The sword dropped to the ground.

Fear overtook him. A fear unlike any he had ever felt. A fear so big and so strong that it paralyzed him. He feared the dragon would put an end to him, and he feared what his life would be like if the dragon *didn't* put an end to him.

The beast had the upper hand, and they both knew it. In fact, all three of them knew it. Prince, being an experienced dragon slayer's companion, diverted their prey's attention by scooting in between it and his master, barking wildly, racing back and forth, and jumping up to nip at its legs.

While the dragon had its hands—or rather its legs—full with Prince, Duke somehow pulled himself up and grabbed for the sword, but it was still too hot to hold. Knowing he had no other choice than to retreat, he limped as fast as he could toward the wagon, looking back over his shoulder to see if Prince was okay and to make sure the dragon wasn't coming up behind him.

The beast soon lost interest in the pesty dog and headed toward Duke, stepping squarely on his lucky sword, which was in its path.

By the time Duke reached the wagon he was exhausted. His ankle was throbbing, his hand was stinging, and the dragon was close behind.

He hurled himself over the side of the wagon and tumbled in. Frantically he grabbed the reins and whistled for Prince, who was still trying to hold back the dragon.

The moment Prince jumped into the wagon the stallions galloped off. The wagon wobbled and bounced over rocks and potholes, tilting first to one side and then the other.

The rain started coming down harder, but Duke kept the horses at a full gallop, wanting to put as much distance between them and the dragon as possible.

Once the dragon was out of sight, Duke glanced quickly at Prince sitting beside him. "Good thing nobody can see their unbeatable team now, huh, boy?" he called out over the sounds of the horses' hooves and wagon wheels. "It wasn't your fault. You did your part."

Suddenly the wagon hit a large pothole and tipped sideways onto two wheels, tossing Duke high into the air—and smack into the trunk of a big oak tree, backside first.

The wagon righted itself and kept on going, wobbling and bouncing as the team of stallions continued at high speed, Prince barking wildly from the front seat.

Duke knew he was injured but couldn't feel much of anything except panic at the thought of his loyal helpmate being carried off by runaway horses. Prince could get hurt, even killed. And what of Duke's beautiful stallions and his one-of-a-kind dragon wagon with all his hero tools in it? There was nothing he could do. At one time he would have taken off on foot after the wagon. But that was when he was as fast as a bolt of lightning, as powerful as a tornado, and able to slay his prey with a single thrust of his sword.

With this thought his mind snapped him back—back onto the ground at the feet of the first dragon that had ever defeated him. The fear washed over him again—fear of the dragon and fear of a life without the thrill of sprinting to the dragon wagon, of racing through cobblestone streets past cheering villagers, of dazzling dragons with his fancy footwork.

A life without all that he loved, without all that he was.

"No!" Duke cried. "I am the number one dragon slayer! I am! And so it *must* be! It must! It must!" He shouted into the now furiously blowing wind. "My life is ruined! This is awful! It's terrible! I can't take anymore!"

Thunder crackled and lightning streaked through the darkened sky. Pellets of rain beat down all around the tree as the dragon slayer sat protected under its giant umbrella of greenery.

"*Now* the storm comes," he muttered sadly, "not that it would have made any difference. I'm in no shape to be fighting dragons, even with the weather on my side."

He removed his face shield and looked down at his tattered, soaked dragon-slaying suit. He sighed and unfastened his chest plate, pulled off his boot, and wiggled his hand from the scorched glove. The ankle was swelling, his hand was blistering, and his backside was so sore he could barely stand to sit on it—which he might have found funny had he not been so depressed.

"This must be what it means to hit bottom—literally," he said, rubbing his aching backside.

Now of all times he needed to do his best thinking, but in his condition he couldn't even pace or crack his knuckles. *My dragon wagon isn't the only thing that has run out of control,* he thought. *My whole life has run amok.*

A few errant salty droplets trickled down his cheeks. With his heart feeling heavier than ever before, Duke raised his hands skyward and looked beyond the branches up into the pouring rain.

"Help me," he cried. "I don't know what to do. If there's anyone or anything out there...please help me."

CHAPTER THREE

An Encounter with the Wise One

Duke called out again and again into the great beyond, trying to empty his heart of its pain.

Suddenly a voice broke through his despair. "When one asks sincerely for help, neither thunder, nor lightning, nor the heaviest of downpours can stop it from coming."

Duke stiffened and looked around. "Who said that?"

"Who? Who? I did," came the reply.

It seemed to be coming from the oak tree Duke had struck. "Where are you?" Duke called out. "In the tree? What are you doing up there? Besides getting soaked, I mean."

"Actually, I was taking a siesta—that is, until the clamor of horses and wagon wheels woke me up just in time to observe you flying through the air and crashing into the trunk of this tree."

"You were taking a nap in a tree? What's the matter with you?"

"Nothing is the matter with *me*. The question is, what is the matter with *you*?" the voice inquired. "*You* are the one who asked for help."

At that moment a large owl descended carrying a black bag in its beak. He placed the bag on the ground, clapped his wings once, and straightened the stethoscope that dangled from his neck.

"Allow me to introduce myself," the owl said in a most dignified manner. "Henry Herbert Hoot, D.H., at your service. My friends call me Doc. As the D.H. indicates, I am a doctor of the heart. I specialize in broken ones, aching ones, and heavy ones."

Duke was speechless. A talking owl? This couldn't be for real. Did he lose consciousness when he hit the tree? He thought about pinching himself to see if he was dreaming but decided he already had too many places that hurt.

Doc had seen that look of disbelief many times. "Everyone reacts that way," he said. "I have something here that will help dispel your doubts."

He stuck his wing into the front pocket of his black bag and, with fingerlike precision, took out some rolled-up parchments fastened with gold ribbons and gave them to Duke. "These are my credentials," he explained. "I carry them with me since I have no office wall on which to display them."

Duke was flabbergasted as he read one and then another, and then another. "Uh-huh. These certify that you're a doctor, all right. That you graduated first in your class from the Kingdom Imperial School of Medicine. And that you satisfied all the requirements for a specialty in matters of the heart."

"Yes, and I also have many letters of appreciation from patients who have had the most perplexing and troublesome problems," Doc added proudly.

Duke was still so overwhelmed that it took him a moment to realize what the owl had said. "Perplexing and troublesome problems. Hmm. I've heard of someone who can solve the most perplexing and troublesome problems. People call him the Wise One. I've wanted to find him for a long time but had no idea where to look. Do you know him, by chance?"

"Well, well. Today is your lucky day," said Doc.

Duke was floored. "First I almost get killed by a dragon, then I almost get killed again by getting thrown into a tree. My magnificent stallions run off with my one-of-a-kind dragon wagon, my irreplaceable sidekick, Prince, and my best hero tools—and you think this is my lucky day! I'd sure hate to see your version of a bad day!"

"Many experiences that seem unlucky at first turn out to have been very lucky indeed. Just think," Doc said, "if you had not been run off by the dragon, you would not have been racing down that road over there. And if you had not been racing down that road, you would not have been thrown into this particular tree at the particular time I was taking my siesta, and you would not have been asking for help—in which case you would not have found me yet."

"You think it was worth going through all that just to find you? Why? Because you know where I can find the Wise One?" Duke asked hopefully.

"No, because I *am* the Wise One," replied Doc, standing tall and holding his feathery head high.

"You can't be!" said Duke indignantly. "You should be a regular doctor type, only with a long gray beard and special powers. Why, you aren't even a person!"

"Everyone knows that owls are wise. In fact, wiser than some people. Often one's teachers look different than one might expect, and it is easy to pass them by without learning what they have come to teach. Teachers come in many forms, some even as unusual as a talking owl."

Under ordinary circumstances Duke would have believed he had finally flipped his wig, which wouldn't have been an easy thing to do since he didn't even have a wig. But these were no ordinary circumstances. This owl was for real, and he was a bona fide doctor. He also had a reputation as a Wise One who could solve almost any problem, and he had lots of thank-you letters to prove it. Besides, Duke was desperate, and it didn't seem like the time to look a gift horse—or gift owl—in the mouth.

"Now let us get down to the reason you flew into my life," said Doc. He smiled slightly, amused by his own quip. "Quite a novelty it is to have someone fly into *my* life for a change. Speaking of change—well, first things first. We will talk more about that later."

Duke didn't want to talk about change or anything else for that matter, except how to get rid of the heaviness in his heart.

"Okay, Sir Wise One—uh, Doc. I really need your help. Nothing is the way it should be. Everything is so awful! I'm desperate! My heart is so heavy it's ruined my life! My used-to-be wife threw me out of my castle, my son told me he doesn't want to be a dragon slayer, and my once-upon-a-time girlfriend walked out on me. I started toppling over and bumping into—no, first my heart got heavier and I got slower and—and *then* I started toppling—never mind, I said that already. Then my fancy footwork turned into . . . Oh, I didn't tell you who I am. You may have heard of me. I'm Duke, the number one dragon slayer in the land—at least I was until today. Well, I guess I still am, sort of. I mean no one knows what happened yet, maybe. I don't know! I don't know! I can't lose my title! It's my life! I was meant to have it. I can't live without it! And poor Prince. I miss him so."

Duke gasped for air. "Wait. I'm getting it all mixed up and leaving out some important stuff. I can't even tell it right. I can't do anything right anymore. Should I start over?"

"No need to," Doc said gently. "I know all about you. As I mentioned before, I am an expert in heavy hearts. That is why I was the one who answered your call for help. Actually, I was expecting you. I just was not sure where or when."

"I don't know how you know all about me, but then I don't know how you can talk or be a doctor, either. No wonder they call you the Wise One. Well, if you know all about me, then you know I'd do anything to get rid of this heaviness in my heart." Duke clutched his chest.

"Do you mean that? You are willing to do *anything*?"

"Yes! Yes! Anything. Even get my heart fixed by a doctor who's an owl. It's my only hope."

"It is fortunate that you are willing to do your part because I cannot simply fix your heart for you. Only you can do that."

Duke was taken aback. "Me? If I could fix it, don't you think I would have by now?" he retorted. "Would I be sitting here with my whole life turned upside down and inside out? I feel like a ship being tossed in stormy seas, churning, churning. I have no peace. And I can't have any until you get rid of this heaviness in my heart and make me strong and fast again and able to fight dragons the way I used to, and you solve my problems with Allie and Cindy and Johnny."

The owl stroked his chin with his wing. "Exactly what problems are you referring to?"

"Well, the problem with Allie and Cindy is that they're still thinking bad stuff about me and blaming me for everything. It's not that I want them back or anything. It's just that I want them to understand everything was their fault, not mine. And I have one heck of a problem with Johnny. He refuses to become a dragon slayer, and Allie's no help at all. See how much I need you?"

"Hmm," Doc said, nodding thoughtfully.

"Come on," Duke pleaded. "You can solve any kind of problem. Can't you use some kind of magic to make things the way they ought to be, and maybe give me some special medicine that'll lighten my heart?"

"A ship in stormy seas. Hmm…churning. Hmm…a heavy heart," Doc murmured. "Yes, just as I thought. This confirms my diagnosis. You have symptoms typical of heart dis-ease, which has manifested in heavy-heartedness."

"I don't understand," said Duke. "What is heart dis-ease?"

"Generally, one might say it is the opposite of a heart at ease. Technically, the condition is a reaction to adversity—disappointments and losses and such—in which the heart fills up with negative emotions. In Type I heart dis-ease, the reaction is appropriate and manageable. The sadness or anger and various symptoms, while very uncomfortable, tend to subside in time."

"But they haven't subsided. They've gotten worse and worse, and my life is such a mess."

"That is usually indicative of Type II."

"Type II? What's that?"

"In Type II, one reacts to adversity by filling the heart with more extreme negative emotions than in Type I—anguish, great anxiety, rage, and often excessive frustration, fear, and pain. As these potent feelings build up, one's heart becomes heavier and heavier. When the condition becomes severe, it can result in myriad symptoms, including but not limited to a noticeable reduction of energy, strength, speed, stamina, concentration, and motivation."

Duke thought for a moment. "Well, I've had all of those."

"Yes, and some sufferers incur potentially serious secondary complications as well, such as a disturbance in balance, resulting from a significant increase in weight concentrated in the left front quadrant of the chest—which you have also experienced. Falls and other injuries are common. This is such a difficult condition for sufferers to manage that they often resort to extreme measures, which can further complicate their condition and their lives—as you also know firsthand."

"Yeah, that's for sure," Duke muttered in disgust.

Doc went on. "Although Type I and Type II may seem to differ only in degree, and neither displays any demonstrable pathology, there are some important differences in both their etiology and their prognoses."

"Would you repeat that again, slowly?" Duke asked, his head spinning. "On second thought, no. I don't think I could take it."

Doc waited patiently, knowing that hearing one's diagnosis can be overwhelming at first.

A moment later Duke said, "That proves it. I knew this heavy heart was all their fault." He sighed. "If things didn't keep going wrong and would just be the way they should be, if certain people would do what they should do and stop doing what they shouldn't be doing, other people wouldn't be in a state of un-ease, or no-ease, or dis-ease, or whatever, right? Then these other people wouldn't end up with heavy hearts, right?"

Doc tipped his head to the side. "That is one way to look at it. However, there is a lot you don't understand yet."

"Understanding isn't going to change anything."

"On the contrary, understanding changes everything," corrected Doc.

"So does this mean you're not going to do anything about Allie and Cindy and Johnny?"

The owl flapped his wings and stretched his large body. "Your problems with them will be solved in time. However, this is not about *them*. It is about *you*."

CHAPTER FOUR

Prescription for a Heavy Heart

Duke was frustrated. It all seemed so absurd. Who would ever believe that Duke, the number one dragon slayer, was stuck under a tree in the middle of nowhere, all banged up, with Type II heart dis-ease, his life a shambles, chitchatting with some talking owl heart doctor. But absurd or not, this owl was his only hope at the moment. He watched with curiosity as Doc reached into his bag.

"I treat so many cases like yours that I have the orders preprinted," he said, tearing off the top page of his prescription pad and giving it to Duke. It read:

HENRY HERBERT HOOT, D.H.

NAME: *Duke the Dragon Slayer*

ADDRESS: *Bachelor-Pad Rent-a-Castle*

Rx *SERENITY*

DOSAGE: *Take as much as you can,*
as often as you can.

REFILLS: *Unlimited*

SIGNATURE: *Henry Herbert Hoot, D.H.*

"A medicine called serenity?" Duke asked. "I've never heard of it. Is it a tonic that I drink? I know, it's a salve to rub on my chest over my heart. I bet that's it."

"It is neither. It is just plain, old-fashioned, everyday serenity. The peace of mind kind."

"Are you kidding?" Duke snapped, waving the prescription in the air. "How am I supposed to fill this? Unless you know of an apothecary that sells serenity by prescription!"

"Actually I know somewhere better than an apothecary where you can get the serenity you need," said Doc.

Duke shook his head. "I'm not so sure about this whole thing. How do I even know it will work if I get it? I mean it's not even real medicine."

"Oh, serenity is real medicine all right," the owl said patiently. "Long-term studies conducted over many years by the finest scientific minds in the land have consistently shown that serenity is the treatment of choice for most types of heart dis-ease. In fact, it is the only effective and lasting treatment available. A full course of treatment can result in lightheartedness that has not been achieved with any other treatment to date. I have medical extracts of the latest studies in my bag. You are welcome to look at them."

Duke's eyes lit up. "Lightheartedness? Really? Oh, what I wouldn't give to be lighthearted!" he said, thinking about what it would mean to be rid of the heaviness in his heart. If only it could happen. He would again be as fast as a bolt of lightning, as powerful as a tornado, and able to slay his prey with a single thrust of his sword. He would be able to retain his title of number one dragon slayer in the land. And he would no longer be toppling over and bumping into things and forgetting things and—

Then, with a vengeance, came the *what ifs*: What if Doc, the Wise One, kept insisting on treating *him* instead of *them*?

What if he could convince Doc to work his magic on them but instead ended up believing they were right? What if he didn't ever get better? What if he had already lost his title to one of the younger up-and-coming dragon slayers whom he had helped train? He would be a disgrace, a worthless has-been, a nobody. And what if something had happened to Prince? He would be all alone.

The sound of Doc's voice broke through his reverie. "All your most perplexing and troublesome problems will be solved in ways you cannot even imagine. Trust in your treatment. Trust that many others like you have been healed by it. If it is to work for you, you need to believe that it can."

"I'll try," Duke said, somewhat unconvincingly. He looked at the prescription again. "Hey, how did you know ahead of time to put my name and address on this?"

"I told you, I knew all about you long before we met." Doc clapped his wings. "Now, Duke, I suggest you get started. A moment wasted is a moment lost forever."

"Get started? Do you mean get started going to that place you said is better than an apothecary? And please don't tell me it's some monastery type place with everyone sitting around contemplating their navels—you know, meditating and *Om-m-m-m-m-ing*. I hate all that mumbo-jumbo stuff!"

"There you go again with your preconceived notions about things. First about teachers, then about the nature of the medicine, and now about how and where you will get the serenity you need. As you soon will see, there is much more to serenity than meditating in a monastery, although that has been found to be quite helpful to some people. Closed minds, close doors. Remember that, Duke."

"Well, whatever the place is, I hope it's close by. Say, do you think you could run—or rather, fly—over there for me and bring back whatever I'm going to need?"

"One cannot receive serenity from someone else, nor can it be bought or attained by demanding it or begging for it. Serenity is a state of being. It is something one must learn how to have," Doc said with resolve.

"Learn? Oh no," Duke groaned. "I thought people just sort of automatically have peace and serenity when everything is going okay."

"That does not always happen. And even when it does, it is not the lasting serenity that sees one through the ups and downs of life."

"You mean you can have serenity when you're down like me and your life is one big, crazy-making, aggravating mess?" asked Duke.

"That is precisely what I mean."

"Did everyone you've helped have to get it—that is, learn it—themselves?"

Doc nodded. "Yes, everyone. I routinely prescribe serenity. Not only will it cure your heart dis-ease, it will solve your other perplexing and troublesome problems.

"Now listen carefully to these instructions," Doc continued. "You are to travel the Path of Serenity and keep an open mind. It winds through two lands. The first is the Land of Serenity. The second, the Land of Courage. Each has a strict law of the land, which you must learn and live by. Then serenity will replace the heaviness that is now in your heart, allowing it to grow lighter and lighter until finally you are set free."

"YES!" shouted Duke, enthusiastically thrusting one fist into the air. "My heart will grow lighter and lighter and I'll be free of its heaviness forever!"

"However," Doc went on, "if you stray from the path or do not complete your journey, your heart will grow heavier again. Partial treatment is not lasting. There are no quick fixes for a heavy heart."

As Duke thought about all he had to do, his enthusiasm began to wane. "When you told me you knew of a better place than an apothecary to get the serenity I need, I thought I was going to one place. Now you're telling me it's a whole path I have to travel, through two lands no less," he said wearily. "How hard is it to learn and live by these laws?"

"Learning them is easy. Living by them is not. But there is a secret, a very important secret, to living them that can ensure your success."

Duke's face brightened. "Tell me, Doc, tell me! What is it?"

"All in good time, Duke."

"Why can't you tell me now? I'm good at keeping secrets, and I really need to know this one."

"This secret takes time to tell, and this is not the time to tell it."

Duke sighed. "Okay," he said, looking down at his swollen ankle and blistered hand. His shoulders were tight and he ached all over. "It really doesn't matter. I can't go anywhere anyway. Look at me. I can't even get myself home."

"I thought you said you were willing to do anything to get rid of the heaviness in your heart."

"I am," replied Duke, annoyed. "Didn't I put ice-cold compresses on my chest, and diet until I grew weak? Didn't I—"

"Yes, yes. I know all about what you tried. It was innovative but not effective. The question is, are you ready to try something different that is sure to succeed if you work at it?"

"I guess I have no choice," said Duke.

"One always has choices. Here are two of yours. You can choose to keep doing as you have been doing, in which case you will keep getting what you have been getting and feeling as you have been feeling. Or you can choose to do something different that will cure your heavy heart and solve your other problems as well. It is entirely up to you."

"Okay, okay. I'll go. I'd go right now, but as you can see, I can't. Not with this swollen ankle and blistered hand, not to mention my backside."

"If they were healed, would you go?"

"Yes, but I would still be too weak and achy."

"If you were stronger and less achy, then would you go?"

"Yes, but first I would have to go find Prince and my horses and dragon wagon and my hero tools so I could take them with me. I don't go anyplace without them. With all that you know about me, you must know that."

Doc looked sternly at Duke. "Apparently, in addition to all your other achievements, you are an accomplished *yes but-er*."

"What's that?"

"It is one who says, 'Yes, I would do this—*but*. Yes, I would do that—*but*.' Excuses, excuses! Where is your number-one-dragon-slayer spirit? You never would have made it had you not found ways around your *buts*."

"Yes, but these aren't excuses!" Duke said, growing more exasperated. They're reasons, real reasons." Then he remembered about the *buts*. "I'm sorry, but I couldn't help saying *but* that time. Oh no—or that time."

"When one has real reasons that one has difficulty overcoming, one can always ask for help," explained Doc, "just as you did when you first called upon me. For some, asking for help takes practice."

Duke was getting exhausted on top of exhausted from all the talking back and forth. He didn't want to say any more *buts*, and he didn't know how to get past them. After thinking for a moment, he said, "I get it. You want me to ask for help in overcoming my reasons. Okay, I'm asking. Can you help me, Doc?"

"I thought you would never ask," Doc replied playfully, reaching into the back pocket of his bag and pulling out a jar of all-purpose salve and a bottle of energizer tonic. "Here, Duke. Apply this salve to your ankle and hand, and to your backside if you are not too bashful, and drink two capfuls of this tonic. That will take care of the first three *buts*."

While Duke was rubbing on the salve and measuring out the tonic, Doc told him that overcoming the fourth *but* was no problem. "You do not have to find Prince or your horses and dragon wagon before you go because you cannot take them with you anyway. And although you will still be fighting a dragon, the granddaddy of all dragons in fact, your old hero tools will not work."

Panic struck Duke. "You didn't say anything about a dragon! You know what happened the last time! This granddaddy had better be a really old one. Even so, I don't think I could do it. Can't you use some kind of hocus-pocus to slay it for me?"

"I am talking about a different kind of dragon, a different kind of fearlessness, and a different kind of fight. Your battle on the Path of Serenity will not be one of swords. It will be one of words."

"How can anyone slay a dragon with words? This is sounding more and more like suicide!"

Duke was too upset to think clearly. Oh, how he missed being able to pace and crack his knuckles.

"Try it," said Doc.

The dragon slayer paused. "Try what?"

"Why, pacing and cracking your knuckles, of course," Doc replied mischievously.

Duke's eyes widened. "How did you know what I was think—never mind," he said, reminding himself to keep reminding himself not to underestimate Doc.

"You really expect me to pace with this," Duke said sarcastically, looking down at his ankle. To his amazement the swelling was gone! Quickly he checked his burned hand. The blister that had covered his palm was gone too. And neither his ankle nor his hand nor his backside hurt anymore either, and he didn't feel as exhausted.

If only my heart could get better that easily, he thought.

"Now I am going to give you something you will find helpful on your journey," Doc announced.

The owl flew high into the tree branches. A moment later he came down with a purple satchel that had Duke's initials and his family crest on the front. He gave it to Duke. "Here are your new hero tools," Doc said. "I cannot slay your dragon for you. However, I can give you the tools to slay it yourself."

"Hero tools!" shouted Duke. "What a relief! Relying on words to slay that dragon isn't too appealing." He held up the satchel admiringly. "Look at this! My initials and family crest! You thought of everything, Doc. Why, it's even the same color as the drawstring bag I keep—or used to keep—my sword in. I don't suppose you made me a new lucky sword, did you?"

"A different mission with a different dragon requires different tools," Doc answered. "Your new mission to get rid of your heavy heart is unlike any you have had in the past. And the dragon you will encounter is unlike any you have fought. It is a stubborn old breed that is well known for threatening people's peace of mind and happiness, so everyone has to be a dragon slayer of sorts."

Duke was so distracted that he hardly heard what the owl was saying. "This is great. I can't wait to see what's in here! Is it okay if I look?" he asked, opening the satchel.

"Yes," replied Doc, "although you may not appreciate their value until you are ready to use them."

"You aren't kidding," said Duke, rifling through the contents, disappointment in his voice. "An empty canteen...eyeglasses...a measuring tape...mittens. Why, this is just a bunch of ordinary stuff."

"Those are no ordinary hero tools. They have special, almost magical qualities that will help you when your need for them arises. There is no point in discussing them now. Hmm . . . magical qualities. Ah, that reminds me of a song," Doc mused, flapping his wings in delight. "Of course a lot of things remind me of songs."

With that, he reached into his black bag and scooped out a miniature banjo and a straw hat, which he placed on his head with great flair. Then he began strumming and singing:

> *It weaves its magic through your life,*
> *No matter how severe your strife,*
> *Even when it cuts like a knife,*
> *It's S E R E N I T Y, S E R E N I T Y.*

> *A heart in pain, a life insane,*
> *Are no match for its power,*
> *It's S E R E N I T Y, S E R E N I T Y.*

> *When the path of life becomes too steep,*
> *And all you can do is sit and weep,*
> *What is this magic many seek?*
> *It's S E R E N I T Y, S E R E N I T Y.*

Suddenly the rain stopped and Duke could hear another voice singing. A moment later a bluebird landed beside Doc, singing with him in perfect harmony.

Duke rolled his eyes. *Nobody would believe this!* he thought.

When the song ended, Duke asked, "How does he know the words to your song, Doc?"

"Actually, *he* is a *she*. It is my pleasure to introduce you to Maxine, my now famous protégée."

"What is she famous for?" asked Duke. "Her harmony?"

"Yes, in a way. She is the Bluebird of Happiness. She has a talent for creating harmony of all sorts. Her greatest gift, however, is creating happiness."

"You mean she's *the* Bluebird of Happiness? I thought she wasn't real."

"Many people think that for some reason," Maxine said, lowering her head demurely. "Even so, I *have* built quite a reputation, thanks to Doc's outstanding tutelage. I'll do all I can to help you through your journey."

Duke looked at Doc with concern. "You mean *she's* coming with me? I thought *you* were. With all due respect to Maxine here, I don't need her to show me how to be happy. I *know* how to be happy. I used to be happy."

"You were happy when everything was the way you wanted it to be," Doc corrected.

"And I'm miserable now because nothing's the way I want it to be. I can't even imagine being happy again—unless everything that's wrong is set right."

Maxine stepped forward. "Happiness doesn't depend entirely on what's happening in your life."

"Oh no," Duke groaned. "Don't tell me she's one of those chin up, smile, and be happy types. Look, Miss Bluebird of Happiness, I'm honored to have met you, and you must be very good at all this happiness stuff. You're famous for it. But the last thing I need right now is to have someone chirping about, trying to cheer me up all the time."

"Not to worry, Duke," Doc said, slipping his banjo and hat back into his bag. "You are in very good hands—or, more accurately, in good wings—with Maxine. She has taken many people on this journey. She knows how to lighten heavy hearts. Remember what I told you about keeping an open mind."

"Well . . . okay, but where are you going to be? What if I need you?"

"As a doctor of matters of the heart my time is very limited. There are others to diagnose and work up treatment plans for, and I have numerous cases in various stages of recovery. I closely follow each, as I will yours. I will check in on you from time to time and will come as soon as I can whenever you call me." Then he grabbed his black bag and flew off before Duke could say another word.

Maxine hopped closer to Duke. "Are you ready to go? You can remove that wet suit and leave it here. You won't need it."

"Are you sure?" Duke asked, reluctant to leave his dragon-slaying suit behind.

"I'm sure," Maxine replied confidently.

Duke shrugged. Taking off his remaining boot, he peeled off the suit, straightened his clothes, sat back down, and pulled both boots back on.

"I'm ready," he said resolutely. "I'd do anything to get rid of my heavy heart—even go on this journey on a wing and a prayer."

CHAPTER FIVE

The Path of Serenity

Duke struggled to his feet, his heart as heavy as ever. He slipped the strap of the satchel containing his new hero tools over his shoulder and plodded out from under the tree into a ray of sunlight peeking through the silvery clouds. *The rain stopped just in time*, he thought.

He turned to Maxine. "So where is this Path of Serenity?"

She smiled as best a bluebird can. "You are already on it."

"You mean the path is right here?" Duke looked up. "I don't see it—"

Suddenly he saw it right in front of him. Duke was stunned. "Where—where did that come from?"

"New paths open when one is ready to travel them," explained Maxine.

"I didn't expect it to look like this," Duke said with disappointment as he surveyed the hilly, rugged terrain. "The Path of Serenity should have flowers and butterflies, not rocks and potholes."

"It is what it is. It would help you to practice accepting rather than expecting."

"How can I accept that it isn't what it should be?"

"By recognizing that it is what it is, and that it will remain what it is, no matter how much you insist it should be something else."

"But it goes up and down and there's all kinds of brush and stuff that'll be hard to get past. I could hurt my ankle again or stumble and fall."

"That's the way the Path of Serenity is."

Still disgruntled, Duke looked around to see what other obstacles he might be facing.

"Look at this!" he said, pointing at a mass of footprints in the dirt. "Lots of people must have traveled this path, but why are some of the footprints coming back toward us?"

"Because some people didn't do what it takes to get the serenity they were seeking," replied Maxine.

"You mean they quit and came back?"

"Yes, with the same problems and more pain than they left with."

"I told you the path was too hard," he said smugly.

"Doing what seems easier at first is often harder in the long run." Maxine took to the air and called out, "Come on, Duke. Let's go."

They set out on the path. Duke pushed himself to take one step and then another, careful not to let the heaviness in his heart topple him. Maxine alternately flew and hopped so she wouldn't get too far ahead.

Before long the brush became so dense that Duke had to push it aside to continue on. "Why hasn't someone cleared this path?" he complained. "I can't see my way."

"I know. That's why you're here," Maxine called down from above.

To avoid such answers Duke decided to ask only simple questions from then on, such as how much farther they had to go before reaching the Land of Serenity. Maxine kept answering, "In good time," which wasn't very helpful.

As he struggled along, listening to the breeze rustling the brush, his mind filled with thoughts—of getting rid of the heaviness in his heart, of being strong and powerful again, of remaining the number one dragon slayer, and of solving the problems with Allie and Johnny and Cindy. He was determined and hopeful.

Then his thoughts turned to strange lands and strange laws, to dragons that could not be slain with a sword, to the path he was traveling that could be fraught with unknown dangers. He didn't know where or when the journey would end—or how. He might not even make it.

As doubt crept in, he began to think about how many people had given up on the Path of Serenity. And the more he thought about it, the more unsure of himself he became.

He stopped and looked at Maxine, who was now hopping alongside him. "Do you mind if I call you Max?" he asked. "Somehow going on this journey with a Maxine doesn't make me confident that my footprints will never be heading back the other way."

"That attitude must make you very popular with the ladies," Maxine said matter-of-factly.

Duke didn't want to think about his popularity with the ladies, especially Allie and Cindy. It was too aggravating. *They shouldn't have treated me the way they did. It was unfair. It was inexcusable. It was—*

Maxine's voice interrupted his thoughts. "If it makes you feel better to call me Max, go ahead. Many people seek strength from others for a while when their own is lagging."

His strength was lagging all right, but depending on a female made him nervous. Their track record so far hadn't been very good. Women were unpredictable and they got upset with him when he hadn't done anything wrong. *If only a woman could be more like a man*, he thought, wondering where he had heard that before. He wished Prince were with him. He would understand. Oh, what he would give to hear his reassuring bark.

Well, Duke realized, he had to rely on someone, and Maxine was the only one there. Anyway, she did know all about the Path of Serenity. And she was, after all, an expert in happiness and had guided lots of people who had heavy hearts—and she had been highly recommended by the Wise One. Okay, he decided, he would call her Max, try not to think about her being female, and hope for the best.

After a while the path started going uphill. Duke's tendency to topple forward worked in his favor for a change, but his extra weight made walking difficult and he had to hold on to his satchel to keep it from slipping off his shoulder. He had not been on the path for long, and already he was growing tired.

"Remind me why I'm doing this," he muttered.

"You know why. Because this path leads to serenity. You don't want to lug around that heavy heart forever."

Just then a gust of wind rose up and brought with it the ringing of a bell somewhere in the distance.

"For whom does the bell toll?" Duke mused, his wit overriding his gray mood.

"It tolls for thee," Maxine replied without hesitation.

"For me? Why?"

"You'll see."

Duke grumbled, "Why do I have the feeling I may not want to see?"

Soon they came upon a small red-brick building surrounded by grass and trees and patches of wildflowers. A tower held an antique silver bell. A raised porch was shaded by a canopy of thick green ivy that had climbed up the front wall and draped itself over the latticework entrance.

"What is this place?" Duke asked.

"See the sign over the doorway?" Maxine said, pointing her wing. "It's the New View Schoolhouse."

"That's a heck of a place for a schoolhouse. It's right in the middle of the path. "Come on," Duke said impatiently. "Let's go around it."

"We can't go around it. Doc said not to stray from the path, remember?"

"But it's *blocking* the path," Duke insisted.

"It is not *blocking* the path. It is *part* of the path."

Duke was in no mood to be delayed. "I've already been to school. I was an excellent student. I learned all my ABCs. That," he said, jabbing a finger angrily at the structure, "shouldn't be here! How are we ever going to get through two lands if we get sidetracked like this? It's so aggravating!"

Maxine flew up and alighted on a nearby tree branch. "You haven't learned the ABCs taught in *this* school, or you wouldn't be in the trouble you're in," she said, wings akimbo.

Duke moaned. "First Doc, now you. You both think I had something to do with causing my own heavy heart, don't you?"

"It isn't your fault that you couldn't prevent it or get rid of it. Without knowing the ABCs taught here, people's emotions are like wayward feathers, tossed about by the slightest breeze. Many develop broken, aching, or heavy hearts, and an assortment of other problems too."

Duke wasn't convinced.

"Look at it this way," Maxine said, a chuckle in her chirp. "You'll be attending an Ivy League school. Get it? See all the ivy?"

"That isn't funny, Max. This is making me mad!" Duke grunted, grabbing on to the iron handrail and pulling himself up the steps to the front door.

Once they were inside, Duke surveyed the room. It appeared to be a schoolroom. On each side were glass walls, which made it seem as if the patches of grass and the trees and wildflowers were part of the room. One simple wooden chair and desk faced a large blackboard with a high stool in front of it. In the far corner were, oddly enough, a rocking chair and bucket.

Through the glass he could see a wiry-looking man wearing a burgundy plaid shirt. He was on his knees, pulling weeds.

"I might as well rest for a minute while I have the chance," said Duke. He walked over to the wooden chair and dropped into it, setting his satchel on the floor beside him. Maxine flew over to the stool.

Duke gestured at the walls. "Why are those walls all glass?"

"So students can get a clear view of what's going on around them," the bluebird said, shaking her tail. "Get it? Clear view. You'll see that it's most appropriate for a schoolhouse like this one."

"You and Doc are quite a pair with your remarks that are supposed to be funny."

"When people are upset it's hard for them to lighten up in little ways."

"Speaking of lightening up, I want to get on with it."

As if on cue, the door opened and the sound of whistling drifted into the room. In walked the wiry-looking man. Part of his shirt was hanging out, and the knees of his denim pants were stained with grass.

"Hi there," he said cheerfully. "I'm Willie Burgundy." He stuck out his hand toward Duke, then pulled it back quickly when he noticed it had dirt on it. "Sorry about that, but I wasn't sure when you'd show up, and I like to putter around. Did you notice the sign over the doorway? It's hand carved. I did it."

Then he turned to the bluebird, who was observing Duke's reactions. "How's it going, Maxine?"

Duke hoped that what he thought was true, was not true. "Would you excuse us a minute?" he said to Willie.

Willie shrugged and walked over to the rocking chair. He sat down and pulled a small piece of wood and a pocketknife from his breast pocket. He whistled as he opened the knife and began to whittle over the bucket.

"Come here, Max," Duke said urgently. "We have to talk!"

Maxine flew onto the desk, careful to avoid landing on the quill pen sticking out of the inkwell. Duke leaned toward her and whispered, "Tell me he's not the teacher, Max—*please*."

Maxine whispered back, "He is a wonderful teacher. You're lucky to have him."

"But he's a weed puller. And he whistles and whittles," Duke hissed, straining to keep his voice down. "Look at him. Teachers aren't supposed to be like that. They should be scholarly and dignified. This is worse than a waste of time. It's terrible—and downright insulting!"

"I understand why you're upset, Duke," Maxine said sympathetically, "but Doc warned you that your preconceived notions can get you into—"

Duke moaned under his breath. "I can't believe this is happening to me. Doc should've told me. It isn't fair to spring extra stuff like this on me at the last minute. I already have a lot to do on this trip, and I don't know how much longer I can stand lugging around this heavy heart."

Willie rose from the rocking chair and walked toward Duke, snapping the knife closed and slipping it and the piece of wood back into his pocket. "Excuse me. I couldn't help noticing how riled up you are..."

Duke didn't hear a word. He got up and started pacing and cracking his knuckles, his mind running wild with thoughts of how awful and unfair it all is, how it shouldn't be that way, how he couldn't stand it.

Maxine and Willie tried to calm him down but he told them to leave him alone, that they had done enough already.

All of a sudden Duke clasped his hands to his chest. "My heart! It's getting heavier! Do something, Max!"

Willie said calmly, "I can tell you why your heart's getting heavier."

"I already know," Duke snapped, sinking back into the chair. "It's because this schoolhouse has gotten me so upset that my heart is loading up with more bad feelings than it already has. You upset me too. I mean, you didn't exactly do anything. Well, it's hard to explain. Anyway, Doc said I have to get through two lands to get the serenity I need. It's my treatment. That's why I can't be stuck here, learning some stupid ABCs that I never heard of. Don't you get it? I have to get rid of this heavy heart. I just can't stand it anymore."

Willie was firm. "Yes, I get it. But riling yourself up will only keep you from getting what you want. This is all part of your treatment. Let's take a slow, deep breath together. Inhale, one...two..."

Duke was furious. This so-called teacher had accused him of riling *himself* up, when it was the teacher who was doing it—he and his schoolhouse and his ABCs, that is. And Duke didn't want this hickey doodle telling him how to breathe, or anything else for that matter. He wanted Doc.

"Doc! Doc, help me!" he called out. "I need you. Come fast! Hurry, Doc! It's an emergency!"

All of a sudden banjo music filled the room. Startled, Duke turned around. There was Doc, wearing his straw hat and strumming his banjo, his black bag beside him.

"Ah, Duke. You called me before I had my new song ready. I rewrite the lyrics often, as I love to play with the sound of words. I know I get carried away, rhyming here and rhyming there. It is such fun though. Well, here goes."

Willie is known both far and near
As the teacher of society's best.
I chose him above others and summoned him here,
To aid you in your challenging quest.

"All the lines rhyme. I love that!" said Doc, continuing to strum. "Of course the verse could use some work. Well, you get the idea." He began singing again:

His credits are many, his background diverse,
His knowledge is yours for the taking.
If you choose not to learn, you'll only get worse,
A big mistake you will be making.

"Hmm, better," said Doc. "Still needs refining."

Duke scrunched up his face. *Sure needs something*, he thought. Maxine and Willie, however, were thoroughly enjoying the performance. Doc sang:

I ran out of words; this song's for the birds—

Then he stopped. "No offense intended, Maxine," he said, abruptly shoving his banjo and hat into his bag. "Anyway, that is all. Apparently this song is not ready to be sung."

"He's that good, huh?" Duke asked, looking sheepishly at his teacher.

"Even better," Doc answered. "For years he ran the renowned Campground for Lost Travelers, which you may have heard of."

"Yes, yes. I'm sorry, Willie. I had no idea. It's just that you look, well, your clothes—and you whistle and whittle and pull weeds. I thought teachers were supposed to be—uh, well, you know, different."

He glanced at Doc, then back at Willie. "But then, I have a lot of preconceived notions. It's sort of a habit."

"No problem," said Willie. "Most people who come here have some habits that could use changing."

Satisfied that Duke's preparatory lesson was progressing nicely, Doc explained, "It is in the schoolhouse that you will learn the secret I told you about."

"The secret? The secret of living the laws of the lands? Why didn't someone tell me that before? I would have been glad to be here instead of upset that I was being delayed."

Doc nodded. "Good observation. You are beginning to recognize the very thing you are here to learn."

As if a switch inside him had been flipped, the anger and frustration that had had Duke in its grip let him go. "I don't know what you're talking about, but my heart just stopped getting heavier. I don't get it. How did you do that?"

Maxine extended her wing with a flourish and said in her best theatrical voice, "You're on, Willie."

She turned to Duke. "I'll meet you on the other side of the schoolhouse when you're finished."

"I am taking off too," Doc announced. "You and Willie have much to do. Oh my, I did not mean to make a rhyme. Once I am in a rhyming mood there is no stopping me."

He raised his wings and said, "Now remember, Duke, the same way a closed mind closes doors, an open mind opens doors, including the one at the back of this room that will allow you to continue on the Path of Serenity."

With a flutter of wings, both birds took their leave. *I didn't even have time to say good-bye*, Duke thought. *They were gone in the blink of an eye.* Suddenly he realized he was thinking in rhymes too.

"Oh no, now *I'm* doing it," he grumbled.

CHAPTER SIX

𝕷essons for the 𝕳eart

"Okay," Willie said to Duke, motioning toward the desk. "Sit down and let's get started."

He pulled the stool closer to his new student and sat on the edge of the seat. Leaning forward, he rested his hands on his knees. "Tell me," he began, "when you first saw the schoolhouse and heard about the ABCs, how did you feel?"

Duke settled back into the chair. "I was plenty mad and impatient and real frustrated and aggravated," he answered.

"I saw you weren't thrilled about my being your teacher either."

"Well, um..."

"Don't worry about hurting my feelings. Everything that happens here is meant to teach you something."

Duke hesitated, then said, "I felt even angrier and more frustrated. And I was insulted that a person who looked like you and acted like you—sorry—was here to teach a famous dragon slayer like me."

"I'm not surprised. And what about just before your heart started getting heavier? How did you feel then?"

"Let's see...I was pacing and cracking—"

"That's what you were *doing*. How did you *feel*?"

"Oh, uh, I was furious, and so frustrated I thought I'd explode."

"Do you still feel that way?"

"No, not anymore. I feel better. In fact, I feel better about all of this, and I can't wait to find out the secret."

"What changed your feelings?"

"Doc did. He changed my mind about everything—the schoolhouse, the ABCs, and you too. When he said I was going to find out the secret in this schoolhouse, not just learn some stupid ABCs, and that he chose you specially to tell it to me because you're the best teacher, well . . . he calmed me right down and made me feel better."

"So things like the schoolhouse and ABCs, and people like me, and even owls like Doc, make you think what you think and feel what you feel?"

"Of course! That's why I have this heavy heart and haven't been able to do anything about it."

Nodding, Willie cupped his chin in one hand. "So you're saying that Doc changed your mind about everything, but did he? Or did *you* change your *own* mind because of what he told you?"

"That's so nitpicky. Do we have to talk about that?" Duke asked with an exasperated sigh.

"Only if you want to get rid of the heaviness in your heart," replied Willie.

Duke shrugged. "Well, I never thought of it that way, but I guess I did change my own mind."

"And when you changed your mind and took a new view of things, what else changed?"

Duke thought for a moment. "I wasn't as upset and my heart stopped getting heavier."

"Did the schoolhouse and ABCs and I change too?"

Duke furrowed his brow. "Well . . . no," he said, bewildered.

"Now that you mention it, none of the things that were bothering me changed at all."

"That's your first lesson," Willie said, getting up and walking to the blackboard. On it he wrote:

LESSON #1

People are disturbed not by things,
but by the views they take of them.

He picked up a wooden pointer from the chalk tray and tapped the blackboard. "This," he said, "is one of the most important truths you'll ever learn. It's a well-known quotation from Epictetus, a philosopher way back in the first century A.D. He's saying that it's your opinion or thought about something, not the something itself, that is upsetting. Once you understand this, everything else will fall into place."

Thoughts raced through Duke's head. What Willie and this Epictetus guy were saying made sense. Duke's feelings *had* changed when he changed his mind and took a new view of the schoolhouse and the ABCs and Willie—but Willie had better not expect him to change his mind and take a new view of Allie and Johnny and Cindy. He couldn't imagine ever doing that.

He looked anxiously at his teacher. "It's not so hard to change my mind about things that only *seem* bad. But it's different with my used-to-be wife and my son and my once-upon-a-time girlfriend. What they did was bad, even worse than bad. That's why I got all upset and got this heavy heart, isn't it?"

"It may seem that way. They gave you plenty of reason to be upset, but what actually got you all riled up were the thoughts you had about what they did."

"But I thought what I thought because of them!" Duke protested.

"Yes, they triggered the thoughts, but they didn't force you to think them. You had some degree of choice. Every day you choose what thoughts to have, whether or not you realize you're doing it. You could have chosen to take a different, less upsetting view and tell yourself less upsetting things—even though what happened seemed really bad. You wouldn't have been happy, but you wouldn't have been as miserable as you are either."

Confused, Duke shook his head. "I don't know. Something about this doesn't sound right."

"Sit back and relax for a minute, Duke. I'm going to tell you a story," Willie said, putting the pointer down and returning to the stool.

"Once there were three scholars who wanted their sons to follow in their footsteps, but their sons wanted to become warriors," he began.

"The first father decided that his son's happiness was more important than his becoming a scholar. This father didn't get a heavy heart. He treated his son with acceptance and respect, and their relationship flourished.

"The second father was disappointed but realized his son has a right to choose the life he wants. This father got a Type I heavy heart but soon got over it. His relationship with his son survived his disappointment, and it, too, flourished.

"The third father thought it was unthinkable, the worst thing in the world that his son wanted to become a warrior instead of a scholar. This father was devastated and developed a Type II heavy heart. He treated his son with anger and resentment, and he received anger and resentment in return."

Willie leaned forward and looked intently at Duke. "These fathers saw the same situation differently and they thought different thoughts about it. Different thoughts led to different feelings and actions.

"The first two fathers *preferred* that their sons become scholars. That left room for compromise, for alternatives when the sons decided to become warriors. The fathers still *wanted* things a certain way but realized they don't *have* to be that way.

"The third father *demanded* that his son become a scholar. He thought things *had* to be the way he *wanted* them to be. And when they weren't, he thought it was *awful* and *terrible* and he *couldn't stand it*. He was devastated and got a Type II heavy heart. The reactions of the first two fathers were appropriate and healthy. The reaction of the third was extreme and unhealthy."

Duke lowered his head and remained silent as the realization sunk in that he too had demanded that his son become something he didn't want to be. He too thought it was awful and terrible and couldn't stand it. And he too was devastated and had gotten a Type II heavy heart.

He looked up at Willie, hesitatingly. "Are you saying my reaction to Johnny's not wanting to become a dragon slayer was extreme and unhealthy, like the third father whose son didn't want to become a scholar?"

"Well, wasn't it? And so was your reaction to the situations with your wife and girlfriend. How else did you get that heavy heart and a life run amok?"

Duke squirmed in his seat.

"When something happens that you don't like, it's natural to have upsetting thoughts about it. But it's these *thoughts*—not what *happened*—that cause you to become upset. That is your first lesson, remember?"

"You mean thoughts can make you get that upset? As upset as I got?"

"Sure can. The more upsetting your thoughts, the more upset you feel, and the heavier your heart gets. If you *think* whatever happened is the end of the world, it will *feel* like it is. That's typical of people with Type II heart dis-ease."

"That's the type Doc said I got."

"Not everybody in your situation would have gotten it, and not everybody's life would have run amok. Yours didn't have to either. You had a choice, the same as those fathers did."

"A choice?" Duke said indignantly. "It sure didn't seem like I had a choice."

"But you did. You could've taken a different view of the things that happened to you and told yourself less upsetting things about them, and you would've felt less upset."

Duke shook his head in disbelief.

"Look," Willie tried to explain, "how do you suppose some people get through all kinds of situations—even tragic ones—better than other people? They can't control what happened, but they can control their reactions by choosing to take a healthy view of it."

"I can't believe this. I'm so frustrated! My head tells me you're probably right, but I still remember how awful it felt when Allie and Johnny and Cindy upset me—and they still do."

"Look around, Duke. They aren't even here. How can they be upsetting you now? They're busy somewhere else living their lives, and have been for a long time. They're not doing anything to you. They may not even know or care how you feel. You got yourself upset over them and you have kept on upsetting yourself—all by yourself. Think about it."

"But every time I think about them and everything that's happened—"

"Exactly my point. Your thinking is what's stirring up your emotions—and keeping your heart heavy."

"But what about when I'm not thinking about it? I still feel terrible and have a heavy heart."

"That's because part of you is thinking about it even though you're not aware of it. Beliefs hidden in the deepest part of your mind affect how you see things and how you feel."

Duke sat silently, the strain building in his face. Suddenly he bolted out of his chair, extra weight and all, and began pacing and cracking and ranting and raving. "My choice. Humph! Hidden beliefs! My patootie!" And on and on he went. Soon the yelling turned to muttering, the pacing slowed, and the cracking stopped. Eventually Duke slumped back into the chair and buried his head in his hands.

Finally he looked up. His eyes were moist with tears. "I came all the way out here just to find out that I've been the one to blame all along."

Willie walked over and laid a hand gently on Duke's shoulder. "You are responsible but not to blame. Blaming yourself will lead to guilt that will only make you more depressed and your heart even heavier—and it won't do anything to solve your problems."

Duke dropped his head back into his hands and mumbled, "I don't know. Everything you've said is swimming around. Nothing's the way it's supposed to be. It's all so awful, so terrible! I can't stand it."

"Duke, you're doing it again—*awfulizing* and *terribilizing*. You're saying things to yourself that rile you up for nothing. Even when very bad things happen, what good does it do to get yourself all worked up about it? Does it change what happened? Does it make you able to deal with it better?"

"I don't know. I can't help it."

"You *can* help it. That's the point. Telling yourself that things shouldn't be the way they are and exaggerating them into holy horrors by saying they're awful and terrible will only hurt you more. And what good does it do you to insist that you can't stand it when in fact you are standing it, aren't you? You're still here. The world hasn't come to an end."

"I guess not," Duke groaned. "But you know what I mean."

"I do know, but this extreme, unhealthy, crooked thinking has boxed you into—well, you can see for yourself. Take out the book that's on the shelf under your desk and look at the first page."

Duke pulled out the book. The cover read:

Lessons for the Heart
The Secret of Living by the Laws of the Lands

Wondering why it took a whole book to tell about one little secret, he turned to the first page. Perplexed, he looked up at Willie. "There's nothing on it."

"Look again," Willie said softly.

"Hey, how did that get there?" Duke asked, as he stared disbelievingly at a picture of a bulging heart behind a row of heavy crooked lines. The heart had a turned-down mouth and sorrowful eyes filled with tears. Below it the caption read:

Crooked thinking = A heavy heart and a life run amok.

"That wasn't there before!" Duke exclaimed. "I know it wasn't!"

"Often what's most needed pops up when and where it's least expected," Willie stated, enjoying Duke's reaction. "An old Chinese proverb says that one picture is worth a thousand words. So what do you think is going on in that one?"

Duke shook his head in dismay and focused his attention on the picture. "Those crooked lines look like bars. Why, that poor bulging heart is in a prison."

"Very observant, Duke. Crooked thinking traps hearts

and keeps them trapped in an emotional prison of one's own making."

"That's just how my heart feels," Duke said sadly.

"What do you think is going to happen to the heart in the picture?"

His voice quavering, Duke replied, "It's going to be stuck there forever."

"It doesn't have to be, and neither does yours if you change your view of things and stop that old habit of thinking yourself into a frenzy. Taking a new view has been proven to make people feel better. Give it a chance."

"I don't even know where to start."

"You can start by telling yourself that it's a huge relief to find out you're in charge of your own emotions. That it's good you're the one who caused your heavy heart and made your life run amok—"

"You must be kidding!"

"No, Duke, I'm not kidding," the teacher said firmly. "It's good because if you did it, you can undo it, and you can make sure you don't ever do it again."

Willie's voice got higher and louder. "Think about it. You'll never again be a helpless victim of anything that happens to you. No more pacing and cracking and making your heart heavy. Do you realize how exciting this is?"

"If it's so exciting, why do I feel so bad?"

"That's natural. When people first learn that they're responsible for their own reactions—and lots of their own troubles—it shakes them up. It's easier to keep on blaming others and the universe. But when you realize that having control over your reactions is a good thing, you'll feel better."

"Well . . . if it really can make me feel better," Duke said with a sigh. "But now on top of all my other problems, I have to worry about what I'm thinking all the time?"

"You don't have to worry about it. You simply need to pay attention to it so you can change thoughts that lead to extreme unhealthy feelings like the ones you've had for so long."

"How will I know what thoughts to change and what to think instead?"

"There's a helpful formula that explains what we've been talking about and makes it all clear. Once you learn how to use it, you'll know what to do."

Willie went to the blackboard. "You're going to love this. It's so simple."

"That's a relief. Simple is about all I can handle right now."

Willie picked up the chalk. "While I'm writing this on the board, why don't you write down what you've learned so far in your lesson book."

"Write? In my book?" Duke asked, flipping through the pages. "But these pages are blank!"

"They're blank because people remember lessons better when they write them down themselves."

Shrugging, Duke turned to the second page. He took the quill pen from the inkwell, but the pen was dry—and so was the well.

Seeing his perplexed look, Willie suggested that he try writing anyway. He did, and the pen worked.

Well, I'll be dipped, he thought, noticing his wit had survived his bad mood. *What a great invention!*

When he finished writing, he looked up at the board. On it Willie had written:

Lesson #2
The ABCs of Emotions

A. Adversity: something happens
B. Belief: view, thoughts about what happened
C. Consequences: feelings and actions

"See? I told you it was simple," Willie said. "As simple as A-B-C, and it works for almost anything that comes up in life. Remember the story I told you? Those fathers faced the same adversity. That was their A. They each took a different view of it, had different thoughts about it, different beliefs—their B. So their feelings and actions, their consequences—C—were different."

Willie put down the chalk and settled back on the stool. "This formula is a truth that doesn't change. Thoughts lead to feelings and actions. Positive thoughts lead to positive feelings and actions. Negative thoughts lead to negative feelings, which may lead to negative actions. And very negative thoughts lead to very negative feelings and may possibly lead to very negative actions. A + B = C."

"Yeah, I see how I got into trouble. A + B = C. That *is* pretty simple."

"It sure is. And now," Willie said in a big voice, "I present to you ... the secret of all secrets. Well, the main part anyhow. Are you ready, Duke?"

"Yes, yes. Finally! What is it?"

Willie turned to the board, and with a grand sweep of his arm wrote:

THE SECRET OF
LIVING THE LAWS OF THE LANDS

What you think is what you feel.

"Ta-da! Isn't that great!" he said excitedly.

Duke's face fell. "That's it? That's the secret? What you think is what you feel."

"Basically, yes. Of course there's more to it. What you think also leads to what you do. And what you do leads to what you think and feel. For that matter, what you think, feel, and do all influence one another."

"But I thought it was going to be a magical secret," Duke said, disappointed.

"This secret works like magic if you work at using it."

"Work at it? You don't understand. I thought it would just somehow automatically make the laws easy to live by," Duke said.

"You know, Duke, quick judgments close your mind. If I were a betting man, I'd bet my whittling knife that this'll turn out to be the best secret you've ever learned."

"I guess that means I need to change my view of it?"

"Right. Then you'll be ready to learn the secret of using the secret."

Duke rolled his eyes. "The secret of *using* the secret?"

Willie fought back a smile and said nothing.

"Okay, teacher, you say this secret works like magic. Let's see if it does."

CHAPTER SEVEN

A New Kind of Dragon-Slayer Bravery

"Now Duke," Willie said, rubbing his hands together, "we're going to look at how you got into the condition you're in and see what you can do about it. Are you ready to use some of that dragon-slayer bravery?"

"I guess so," Duke answered. "What do I have to do?"

"Come to the board and list your ABCs—the things that happened to you that you've been upset about, the thoughts you had about them, and the feelings and actions that resulted."

Willie held out the chalk and Duke pushed himself out of the chair. He took the chalk and wrote:

My A's

My wife told me to leave.
My son refused to become a dragon slayer.
My girlfriend walked out on me.

"Good," Willie said. "Now try to remember the thoughts you had when those things happened, and list them on the board."

Duke cringed. Then, beginning with Allie, he wrote:

My Bs

She can't do this to me!
This is awful!
I ought to be home where I belong!
She messed up my whole life!
Things shouldn't be this way!

As his thoughts about her surfaced, an avalanche of similar thoughts about Jonathan and Cindy came up too—and overwhelmed him. Pained and puzzled, he stopped writing. "All this thinking about thinking about thoughts is getting my mind all jumbled up. This is more thinking and thoughts than I ever thought I would think about."

He sighed and turned back to the blackboard, writing as fast as he could and pressing so hard that twice he broke the chalk and had to use a new piece.

Johnny must become a dragon slayer!
It isn't right for him to refuse!
It's not fair!
Everything's all wrong!
I don't deserve this!
This is all so terrible!
I can't stand it!

The sound of Willie's voice cut through the flurry of thoughts Duke was purging onto the board.

"Okay, that's enough," Willie said. "Now let's talk about some of these thoughts." He pointed at the list. "See here . . . and here . . . and here. You told yourself that things *should* be—*must* be—different from what they are and that it's *awful* and *terrible* that they're not and you *can't stand it.* You turned your *wants* into *musts, absolutes, demands* that could not be met, like the third father in the story. He was so devastated over his son wanting to become a warrior instead of a scholar that he got a Type II heavy heart, remember?"

"You know, before you told me that story I would have said that anyone would have thought what I did," Duke commented. "Now I know it's possible to see things differently, but I still can't—and somehow I think anybody in my situation would feel the same way I do."

"Not everybody whose wife tells him to leave, whose son is not the way he wants him to be, or whose girlfriend walks out is in the condition you are. Some people endure far worse and still don't do to themselves what you have done to yourself."

Willie paused for effect. "Pardon me for being blunt, but not everybody drags themselves around with a Type II heavy heart, moaning and groaning and whining and carrying on like a spoiled, demanding child who isn't getting his way."

Duke was incredulous. "I do that?" Then he sighed. "Never mind, I guess I do."

"Yes, and acting like that won't get you anywhere, except deeper into trouble. Sometimes you simply have to make peace with what happened and move on the best you can. Remember that young dragon slayer a few years ago who was seriously injured in a chariot race? He could've sat around forever complaining and carrying on about his bad luck and his bad legs, and done nothing. But did he? Absolutely not. He felt angry about what had happened to him, and he was sad that his career as a dragon slayer was over, but—"

"See!" Duke cut in, poking his finger at Willie. "He didn't just tell himself it was okay he was hurt in that accident, that it was no big deal. He thought stuff that made him plenty upset. Don't tell me he didn't get a heavy heart!"

Willie was unruffled by Duke's outburst. "What he thought and felt was understandable and healthy under the circumstances," he went on calmly. "It was normal for him to feel upset and heavyhearted, especially at first—the same as it was normal for you. But he didn't *get* so upset and *stay* so upset that he gave himself a Type II heavy heart and a pile of other problems. Do you recall what he did do?"

"Yeah," Duke replied without enthusiasm. "He founded that council for safety in chariot racing and got some famous people to serve on the board. He asked me if I wanted to be on it but I was away too much. Uh, George, that was his name. He also became a chariot race announcer. I thought the accident had made him crazy when I heard him say he was happier than he'd ever been slaying dragons and that he had his accident to thank for it."

"Adversity often bears unexpected gifts. One day's difficulties can be the next day's blessings."

"I guess George thought so. How did he turn everything around like that anyway? Was he one of your students, Willie?"

"I can't say. Teacher-student confidentiality, you know. But I can say that he must have viewed his situation as positively as possible to feel as good as he does about it. Remember, positive thoughts lead to positive feelings and actions."

"Mm-hmm, the secret, A + B = C," Duke said, nodding. "But I don't know. It's still hard to believe he could have such a bad thing happen and end up so happy."

"That's because he had a lot more going for him than just positive thoughts. He made his accident count for something. He learned from it and found a way to get some good out of it—for himself and for others. Taking positive action helped him to feel better and think straighter. That, my friend, is a ticket to happiness."

Duke scratched his head. "So his thoughts helped him do something positive, and doing something positive helped him think straighter, and his thinking and doing helped him feel better, and feeling better helped him think straighter and do what he did. Yeah, I get it. Everything does work together, just like you said. It's all part of the secret you taught me. Maybe George wasn't so crazy after all."

"Now you're seeing the whole secret in action." Willie said, picking up a piece of chalk and drawing a crooked line next to each of the thoughts that Duke had listed on the blackboard.

"Why are you doing that?" Duke asked.

"To show that these are irrational crooked thoughts, the same kind of crooked thoughts that trapped the crying heart in your book, remember? They are opinions, beliefs, not facts. But they sound like facts—absolute, for-sure facts. Let's see what feelings and actions they led to."

Grateful to stop thinking about his crooked thinking, Duke took a deep breath and began writing.

My Cs

Furious, very frustrated, very hurt
Paced and cracked a lot more than usual
Got a Type II heavy heart and could hardly
*   drag myself around*
Distracted: dropped things, bumped self, forgot
*   where I put things*
Started having problems slaying dragons and
*   lost my confidence*
Tried to drown my troubles in juice and got
*   thrown out of my castle again*

Nearly got killed trying to fight a dragon
Nearly got killed running away from a dragon
Depressed, helpless, desperate

The more Duke thought about how bad he had felt and all the problems he had had, the more the painful feelings welled up inside him again. Suddenly he threw down the chalk and started pacing and cracking.

"I was furious—and I still am!" he blurted out. "I'm so frustrated I could burst. How dare they do this to me! None of this ever should have happened. It isn't fair! It isn't right!"

He clasped his hand to his mouth and froze, his eyes opening wide in anticipation. Sure enough, a moment later he clutched his chest. "Oh no! My heart! My heart! It's getting heavier again! I shouldn't have said all that stuff! It's doing it to me again! I knew it! This is awful. It's terrible. I can't stand it!" he cried, pacing frantically, wishing he could crack his knuckles, but he couldn't because one hand was still clutching his chest.

"Duke! Duke! Stop awfulizing and terribilizing!" shouted Willie. "Look at what you're doing to yourself!"

But Duke was so caught up in his pain and in the struggle to stop saying what he was used to saying that he didn't realize Willie was talking to him.

"Duke . . . Duke . . . DUKE!"

"WHAT?" he shouted back.

"STOP! Pay attention to what you're thinking!" demanded Willie. "Stick your hand out in front of you and say 'Stop!' to your crooked thoughts."

"Like this?" Duke came to an abrupt halt, thrust his hand out in front of him, palm out, and bellowed, "STOP!"

"Yes! Words have consequences, you know. They're very powerful."

Exhausted, Duke tried to catch his breath. "I sure hope so. Doc said I have to use them to fight a dragon."

"Don't worry, the right words can slay even the most troublesome dragons in anybody's life, but the wrong ones will bring defeat."

"Well, what are the right ones?" Duke asked, growing agitated again. "Tell me quickly! My heart's still getting heavier!"

"You can stop it. Do as I say. Take a slow, deep, calming breath."

"You and that breathing business again. Okay! Okay!"

Duke took a deep breath. Willie instructed him to do it again, and again.

"Now you're ready. Let's get some straight thoughts in there—fast. Those *shoulds* and *musts* and *awfuls* and *terribles* and *I-can't-stand-its* are doing you in." On the blackboard Willie scrawled:

Your New Bs

I don't like what Allie and Johnny and Cindy said and did, but it's not awful or terrible. It's just too bad, and I can stand it!

He drew a straight line next to the new straight thought. "Now read this aloud, Duke, and say it as if you mean it."

Duke nearly choked trying to get out the words.

"Say it again, stronger," Willie instructed. "Rational straight thinking like this will solve your heavy-heart problems. Come on, say it."

Duke complied. "There, I said it."

"That's still too weak. Say it again, as if you very strongly believe it."

"But I *don't*!" shouted Duke.

"You will. You're still learning. For now, just pretend that you believe it and say it again, stronger. Put some emotion into it."

Duke swallowed hard and shouted out the words as loudly as he could.

"That was much better," Willie assured him. "Here are some other thoughts you can choose that will help you to be less upset."

He wrote four more new straight thoughts on the board:

What's happened to me seems unfair, but life's not always going to be fair.
Things don't have to be the way I want them to be, even though I'd prefer it.
People don't have to treat me the way I want them to, although I'd be happier if they did.
I absolutely refuse to make myself miserable about the things that have happened.

Willie drew a straight line next to each new thought. Then he urged Duke to force himself to say them again and again as convincingly as he could.

Finally Duke declared, "I still don't believe all this stuff, you know."

"That's okay," Willie said patiently. "Start again."

Duke went back to the beginning of the list and repeated each new thought until it sounded forceful enough to satisfy Willie. Suddenly he blurted out, "It worked! My heart stopped getting heavier! That's amazing! How did that happen?"

"You stopped yourself in the midst of making your heart heavier and started straightening out your crooked thinking, changing *shoulds* and *musts* to *wants*, and *awfuls* and *terribles* to *too bads*."

"I did? Yeah, I did!" Duke said, beaming.

"You sure did. You have control of it. You made your heart get heavier and you made it stop. Your new thoughts led to new feelings, and your new feelings affected your body. How do you feel now?"

"Disappointed...sad...frustrated, but not so upset that I can't stand it, I think. I still don't feel good but I feel a lot better, and calmer."

"Good for you, Duke. Your disappointment, sadness, and frustration are healthy because they're appropriate to what happened. They may not feel good, but they won't give you a Type II heavy heart or make your life run amok."

"I've got to sit down," Duke said, heading for his chair.

Willie wrote:

Your New Cs

Calmer
Heart stopped getting heavier
Disappointed
Sad
Frustrated

Willie pointed to the old B and C lists. "See how these crooked thoughts made you feel upset?" Then he pointed to the new B and C lists. "And how these straight thoughts made you feel less upset?"

Duke wiped his brow with the back of his hand. "I do, but straight thoughts are a lot easier to talk about, and to write, than to think. I had to say them over and over to get them to work."

"That's the way it is when you're new to the ABCs. You sometimes have to work hard at convincing yourself. Practice is the key. In fact, that's your homework."

"Homework?" Duke grumbled. Then, remembering to think about his thinking, he stuck his hand out and said, "Stop!" He took a slow, deep, calming breath. "Okay, it's not awful or the end of the world to do some homework. I guess I can stand it. It'll help me get better at doing this."

Smiling, Willie put down the chalk and brushed the dust from his hands. "That's the idea. Now copy the ABCs into your book, both the old and new lists, so you can remind yourself what to think and what not to think. And of course copy the secret."

Willie ambled over to the rocking chair, took out his knife and piece of wood, and started to whittle. "Be sure to include what we said earlier about words having consequences and being very powerful. That's important to remember." He made a few strokes with the knife. "It's also important to remember to read and say your straight thoughts often, and strongly, and to add new ones as you come up with them."

With a twinkle in his eye, he added, "Now it's up to you whether you're going to be one of those who overcomes adversity, or one who lets adversity overcome you."

He started whistling softly.

Adversity, smursity, Duke thought, opening his book. The image of the bulging, crying, trapped heart greeted him and lingered in his mind as he turned to a blank page and began copying down the ABCs. When he finished he turned back to the heart on the first page and stared and stared at it.

Finally he said, "I'm Duke the Dragon Slayer and I shall learn to win out over crooked thinking just as I learned to win out over dragons. If a dragon slayer–turned–chariot race announcer can do it, I can do it. It's a matter of honor and the thrill of the contest. That's my new view. I shall use straight thinking to free my heart from its emotional prison." Then he drew a large X through the heart.

Suddenly the picture was gone, and a new one appeared in its place—a gently rounded, smiling heart with twinkling eyes and wings on its sides. Straight lines emanated from the heart like brilliant rays of light around the sun. The new caption read:

Straight thinking = A happy heart—and a lighter one.

"Whoa! Look at that!" Duke exclaimed. "It changed all by itself. Little did I know when I first saw the New View Schoolhouse..."

He snapped to attention. "I got it, Willie! I learned the New View lesson in the New View Schoolhouse. And these glass walls are clear for a clear view of the things that happen! How clever!"

Willie looked up from his whittling. "If you think that's clever, wait until you find out what the eyeglasses in your satchel are for," he said mischievously.

"Oh yeah, my hero tools!" said Duke, dropping his pen and nearly falling off his chair trying to grab the satchel off the floor. The chair teetered and threatened to tip over, but planted itself firmly on the floor again when Duke sat back up and plopped the satchel on the desk. He pulled it open and fished around for the eyeglasses.

"Here they are! Look! They have a logo on them—NV. It's not a brand name, is it? It stands for New View," he said excitedly, as if he had made the greatest of discoveries. "And the lenses are clear for a clear view, like these walls, right?"

"Right. Those glasses will help you see with new clarity when your old view comes back and clouds your thoughts about something that happens, or happened, to you."

"Doc said these hero tools have special, almost magical qualities! It's a good thing I have them. The ideas of taking a new view and the ABCs are obvious once you know them. But

I have a feeling that using them on the path isn't going to be easy."

"Some situations will be easier than others," replied Willie. "If you keep using that stubborn dragon-slayer spirit of yours against your old way of thinking, you'll be as victorious as you used to be with dragons."

Willie handed Duke the piece of wood he had been whittling. "Here's a new hero tool that might help."

"A stick? What's it for?" Duke asked.

"To remind you to think straight. You know, straight as a stick. Or is that straight as an arrow? Well, that would've taken longer to whittle. Besides, a stick will fit better in your satchel." Willie smiled.

"You whittled this just for me? I wondered what you were making. Thanks!"

"Glad to do it," Willie said, giving Duke a big pat on the back. "You've earned one of these from yourself too. Your openness and willingness and bravery are commendable."

"Open minds, open doors," Duke said proudly, "even if I still have a few reservations about the trip, huh, Willie?"

At that moment the back door swung wide open.

"How did that happen?" asked Duke, startled.

"It answered your question: Open minds do open doors, even when there are reservations. New experiences await you. Come on, Duke. I'll walk you out. Remember to take your book and pen."

Duke slipped them and the glasses into the satchel, then added the stick. He stood up and slung the strap over his shoulder.

Arm in arm, the student and the teacher walked through the doorway and onto the sunlit path.

The door slammed shut. *Must be in anticipation of the next student,* Duke thought. He thought about what a strange thought that was. *If you aren't already thinking crazy when you get here, you sure are by the time you leave.* Then he thought about thinking that too. "Hey, I'm thinking about my thinking all by myself! I did it before too."

"That's a good sign," said Willie. "You've learned your lessons well so far. You're on your way to the serenity you seek. Of course there will be new lessons to learn. There always are."

"New lessons? Duke said apprehensively. He took a slow, deep breath. "Okay. I'll get through them."

"That's the attitude to take. Now Duke, a word of caution. You need to be prepared. Things are bound to happen on the path that you might not like at first. When they do, remind yourself of how you once felt about the schoolhouse and the ABCs and me, and about George too. And practice, practice, practice changing your crooked thoughts to straight ones. Whatever happens, think of each experience as a teacher and learn the lesson it brings. You may even find a valuable gift in it."

"I'll do it, Willie. Just the way you taught me."

"The road is bumpy but using the ABCs will save your bottom again and again, if you know what I mean," the teacher said with a grin.

Duke knew exactly what Willie meant. His life had become bumpy all right, as bumpy as the road full of rocks and potholes that had tipped his wagon and smacked him bottom first into a large oak tree. He began to tremble at the memory of his encounter that day with the dragon that had sent him running in fear.

Willie put his arm around Duke and gave him a reassuring squeeze. "Facing dragons is part of the journey. You're a good student. You'll do fine."

"I wish I could believe that as much as you do." Duke smiled sheepishly. "Anyway, thanks for everything."

Willie squeezed him again. "Okay, enough is enough. It's time to get going, my friend."

As Duke strode away from the schoolhouse, he heard Willie call out, "Keep up the good work!"

Duke waved and shouted back, "You too, Willie, with your teaching, and your whistling and whittling."

Then, seeing Willie kneeling on the grass, he added, "And with your weeding!"

CHAPTER EIGHT

The Land of Serenity

The moment Duke began to wonder where Maxine was, the bluebird swooped down from the air and landed on his shoulder.

"Under ordinary circumstances I wouldn't ask for a ride," she explained, "but I injured my wings at the hummingbird convention. I know bluebirds can't move their wings as fast as hummingbirds can, but I just couldn't resist entering the contest anyway. It was such fun!"

"You hurt your wings trying to flap as fast as a hummingbird?" Duke repeated, trying not to laugh at the mental image of it. "There was a time when I would've said that's awful. Now, since the schoolhouse, I'd say it's only too bad. Or I might have said that you should've known better, but I'm trying not to say *should* anymore, or any other words that mean *have to* or *must* or anything."

"Well, well! Haven't you come a long way since last we met," said Maxine.

"Yes," Duke answered as they continued down the path. "I learned about the secret! Now I know all about the ABCs and views and consequences and healthy feelings and crooked thoughts. For instance, you seem happy in spite of having hurt your wings. Is that because you're the Bluebird of Happiness? Or is it because you know how to think straight and everything, like Willie taught me?"

"Yes, to both. Interestingly, I wouldn't have become the Bluebird of Happiness had I not become expert at thinking straight and putting my new thoughts into action. You may become a bluebird of happiness one day too, Duke. Many people who travel this path do," Maxine said, a chuckle in her chirp.

Duke wrinkled his nose in distaste. "If doing my lessons is going to turn me into a cheery bluebird, I'd better give this trip some more thought."

"I'm glad to hear you still have your sense of humor. You're going to need it," Maxine said playfully.

"I won't ask what that means. I don't think I want to know."

They continued on in silence except for Duke's occasional impatient question about how much farther they had to go before reaching the first land, and Maxine's reassuring answer that they would be there soon. All the while Duke awkwardly trudged along as fast as his weight would allow, with his little companion swaying and bouncing and gripping his shoulder tightly so she wouldn't fall off when he passed too close to the brush or stumbled into a pothole.

Finally, in the distance, Duke saw a clearing with something in the middle of it. When they came closer he saw it was a big wooden sign. Squinting in the sunlight, he struggled to make out what it said.

WELCOME

TO

THE LAND OF SERENITY

LAW OF THE LAND
Accept the things you cannot change.

"We're here!" he shouted. "And there's the law of the land!"

"Yes, and you need to be extremely careful not to break it," cautioned Maxine. "It's strictly enforced to maintain a serene environment. Once we enter this land, you'll be held accountable for anything you think or say or do that breaks the law, except, of course, during the grace period granted to all newcomers."

"Grace period?"

"Yes, you have the rest of today to get used to observing the law."

"Well, I'd better get started. Let's see, accept the things you cannot change. Accept the things you cannot change. There, I've learned it," he said, walking confidently past the sign and into the peaceful, lush green landscape that lay in front of them. "Now I just have to live by it."

Throwing open his arms, Duke declared, "I accept everything here—the flowers, the trees, the air, the quiet—everything. I accept it all completely."

He turned to Maxine on his shoulder. "It's all so beautiful, there's nothing to change anyway. I was worried that the laws would be hard to learn and live by, but this one doesn't seem so bad. How long will it take for my heart to get lighter? I don't feel anything yet."

Maxine would have raised her eyebrows if she had any. "You really don't think that's all there is to it, do you, Duke?"

He shrugged. "You can't blame a guy for trying."

Maxine smiled. "Accepting things you like—things you wouldn't change if you could—is easy. No one has to learn how to do that. But this law requires you to accept everything in your life that can't be changed, including the things you *don't* like and *would* change if you could."

"Hmm, everything I don't like . . . Well, I don't like what happened with Allie, and I would change that if I could. Are you telling me I have to accept that? I don't think I can. I mean, I learned how to be less upset about it, but it still bothers me."

"It may always bother you—or rather, you may bother yourself about it. But the more you accept that what happened, happened, that there is nothing you can do about it, and that it isn't the end of the world, the less upset you will be."

"Whenever I think about it, though, I want it to be different," Duke insisted.

"Fortunately, people don't *need* everything to be the way they *want* it to be."

"So I've heard."

"Maybe you've also heard there's no use wanting the past to be different. The past has passed. You can't unring a bell."

The words stuck in his mind. *You can't unring a bell. You can't unring a bell.* Suddenly the truth of it washed over him like a giant wave.

Maxine recognized that I-get-it look. "Are you ready to accept that what was, was—and stop fighting it?"

Duke contemplated his situation. It was undeniable that he had tried not to accept the past, and look where it had gotten him. If accepting it would help get him the serenity he needed, he would do it.

"Okay. I can't change the past, so I will accept it." Once more he threw open his arms and exclaimed, "I hereby accept the past, now and forever."

Then he looked at Maxine. "Now will my heart start getting lighter?"

"Not yet, Duke. It's one thing to decide to accept the past. It's another to do it. That will take practice, and so will accepting the present."

"Willie had me practice changing crooked thoughts to straight ones, and it stopped my heart from getting heavier. It was amazing, but it didn't last. The crooked thoughts keep popping back into my head, even though I've replaced them again and again with straight ones. It's exhausting—crooked thinking, straight thinking, crooked thinking, straight thinking, crooked—"

"You've been thinking crooked for years. It takes time for old automatic thinking to change. But if you keep practicing, you won't get upset as easily, as often, or for as long—about Allie or your son or anything else."

As they walked on, Duke was deep in thought. He muttered, groaned, grimaced, and even shouted from time to time. Before long these were replaced by a steady look of determination and an occasional triumphant smile.

"I see what you mean about practicing. I've been thinking about Allie and I can see how this might work."

"Okay, now let's talk about something else you need to accept."

"Do we have to?" Duke whined.

"Only if you want to get rid of the heaviness in your heart."

"That sounds familiar. You and Willie must spend a lot of time together."

Maxine would not be diverted. "How about your son's not wanting to become a dragon slayer?" she asked cautiously.

Duke stopped walking and glared at her. "Oh, not that. It would be a big waste of time to change my *shoulds* and *musts* to *prefers*, and my *awfuls* and *terribles* to *too bads* and all that when it's still possible to change Johnny's mind—I mean, for me to get Johnny to change his own mind. He could still be different if he'd just try hard enough. I know he could. You don't want me to waste my time forcing myself to accept something that can be changed, do you? Let's work on Allie some more or on Cindy or on my giving myself a heavy heart or something."

Maxine replied gently, "People can't change other people. You tried for years to change your son, to get him to be what you thought you needed him to be. If wishing and pacing and cracking and yelling could get him to change, don't you think it would have already?"

Duke's mind was spinning. "I—I have to sit down. No, I don't. I have to think. No, no, I'd better not—oh no!" he said, grabbing his head in his hands. "Johnny *has* to become a dragon slayer. He *has* to be number one."

Duke looked up pleadingly. "Tell me he'll follow in my footsteps and in those of my father and his father before him. Max, please! Tell me!"

Being a smart bird—and well trained—Maxine knew what to do. "Quick, Duke, tell your crooked thoughts to stop!"

Duke thrust his hand out and shouted, "STOP! STOP RIGHT NOW!"

He cringed from the sound of his voice reverberating through the quiet. He took deep, calming breaths, and Maxine helped him come up with some new straight thoughts: "I would strongly *prefer* that Johnny become a dragon slayer but he doesn't *have* to. If he doesn't, it won't be awful or terrible and I'll be able to stand it. I absolutely refuse to make myself all upset about this. And I refuse to be like that third father anymore!"

Duke panted, out of breath. "Whew, that was close, Max. It's a darn good thing I have a grace period!"

"See, your lessons are working already and you've barely

scratched the surface of their power. Now let's keep going. It's getting late and there's a lovely rest area coming up. See it?"

She fluttered her wings and lifted herself off Duke's shoulder. "It's time for me to make a test run."

As Duke watched, the bluebird fluttered faster and faster, gaining altitude briefly, then dipping down, barely staying airborne. Finally she crash-landed on a stone bench at the entrance to the rest area. Duke ran over to her.

"My wings feel better but they're a little stiff," Maxine called out. She seemed to have gotten a kick out of the flight. Duke collapsed beside her, holding back a smile.

Maxine composed herself. "This bench is hard because it's made of stone, and the nature of stone is to be hard. Stars shine because it's their nature. Whether or not you can see them shine, believe they ought to shine, or demand that they not shine, they go right on doing what they were made to do—express their nature. Trying to get people to change their nature is almost as useless as trying to get stone and stars to change theirs."

There was a lump in Duke's throat that felt so large he wasn't sure he could get his voice past it. "Are you saying it's useless to try to get Johnny to change?"

Maxine looked up at him compassionately. "Well, for years he tried as hard as he could to be good at fencing and javelin throwing and to enjoy hero stories, but it may be his nature to be better at chess and to prefer lectures. No matter how hard people try, they usually can't change their basic natural tendencies. That's just the way it is. Stone is hard and stars shine."

"How, Max?" Duke moaned. "How do people accept the unacceptable?"

"By developing the serenity to be able to, and then deciding to, and then working at doing it."

"You mean I have to *have* serenity to *get* serenity? How

am I supposed to do that? It's like that old saying, Which came first, the chicken or the egg?"

"You can do it by doing just what you have been doing—calming yourself down with straight thinking, taking a new view of things, and using your ABCs to take acceptance into your heart and make it part of you. You know, many people ask for help the way you did, under that tree."

Duke nodded slowly, tears welling up in his eyes. "Stone is hard and stars shine, and I guess my son can't be me. It isn't his nature. He's not a Johnny. He's never been a Johnny. And he's probably never going to be a Johnny. He is a Jona . . . a Jonath—oh, what am I going to do? I can't even say it. How can I possibly be ready by tomorrow?"

A thought flashed across the darkness in Duke's mind. "When Allie and Cindy tried to get me to change, I told them that I am who I am. So I was right, right? They refused to accept my nature, right?"

"No, Duke. It wasn't your nature they were objecting to, only your attitude and the way you were acting. They weren't asking you to change what you're naturally good at or what you enjoy doing. They didn't say you should change your whole personality—the things that make you you."

"MAX! STOP, STOP!" he yelled, frantically waving his arms. "You can't say shou . . . shou—the S word! You shou . . . shou—the S word—know better. You're going to get us into terrible trouble. Oh no! I said terri . . . terri—"

The sight of Duke flapping like a bird struck Maxine as hilarious, and she began to giggle in her distinctive chirpy style.

"What's so funny, Max?" Duke asked defensively.

"Oh, you just pushed my silly button, that's all!" she choked out, falling onto her back on the bench.

"I—I'm sorry. I didn't mean to," he replied nervously.

"Hey, what's a silly button anyway?"

She tried to answer but all that came out were bursts of giggles, which only made her giggle more. She giggled harder and harder, rolling back and forth until she rolled right off the bench.

Astonished, Duke peered over the edge of the seat. There was Maxine on the grass, still rolling and giggling with wild abandon.

"I can see why they call you the Bluebird of Happiness," he called out over her chirps of delight. "Either your title fits you amazingly well or there's a juice bar around here somewhere that I don't know about."

Still giggling a little, Maxine sprang to her feet and fluffed her feathers. "There's more than one way to lighten up, Duke. I learned a long time ago about the importance of a good laugh, especially when life is testing your mettle. You might give it a try one day."

For a smart bird she sure acts nutty sometimes, Duke thought. "Now that you've had your fun, can you tell me why you said that *S* word we're not supposed to say?"

"Sure. I'm allowed to use outlawed crooked thinking words for teaching purposes. In fact, you're allowed to use them too, for purposes of discussion. You are, after all, in this land to learn."

As the sun dropped lower in the sky, Maxine led Duke to a nearby tree. Beneath it was an inviting bed of leaves and a basket filled with biscuits and colorful, succulent-looking fruits and vegetables. Duke hurried over to the basket and grabbed a golden pear from the top.

"Where did the basket come from?" he asked, taking a big bite of the fruit and sitting down on the leaves.

"The Path of Serenity provides many kinds of nourishment."

Duke decided the food would be a lot more satisfying than trying to figure out what Maxine's answer meant, so he let it go and reached for a biscuit. He ate eagerly while Maxine pecked around in a patch of grass, searching for her usual sustenance.

When they had had their fill, she suggested that he get to work on his new straight thoughts before dark. He opened his satchel, took out his pen and his book of lessons for the heart, and flipped to the list he had copied down at the schoolhouse. He added the new straight thoughts he had come up with earlier and those Maxine had helped him think of. Then he read the entire list aloud, repeating each thought several times, with Maxine saying, "Stronger, stronger, put some feeling into it. Convince me, convince yourself, convince the world you mean it!"

After he finished, Maxine whistled and clapped her wings together in applause. "Very good, Duke. Now I have something to give you. I'll be right back."

Duke placed the book and pen back in his satchel, and a few moments later Maxine returned carrying something in her beak. It was a beautiful silvery stone.

"What's this for?" Duke asked as Maxine placed the stone in his hand.

"It's a hero tool."

Duke turned the stone over and over. "Very clever, Max. The stone is hard and it shines like the stars."

"Yes, things are what they are and people are who they are. What is, is, and what was, was. Now it's time for us to settle down for the night."

Pointing to the branches overhead, she said, "My bed of leaves is up there."

Duke looked up into the branches. "Max, have you ever fallen from a tree while you were sleeping?"

Maxine giggled. "Why, Duke. When was the last time you saw a bird fall from a tree?"

"But what holds you up there?"

"My foot, of course."

"One foot? You sleep on one foot?"

"Yes, I prefer my left. Most birds do, although there are quite a few right-footed birds."

"I don't get it. It was hard enough to believe *two* feet could hold you up there. How can you possibly stay up with *one*?"

"Easy. I have a built-in, fail proof ratchet system, compliments of the universe," she said, readying her wings for takeoff.

"Wait! Don't go yet. I've always wondered about this."

"Wonder no more. It's automatic. I pick my spot. I squat. My foot grips. It locks. That's it. Sleep well, Duke. See you in the morning."

She flew up, dipped a little, then up again and disappeared into the branches above.

Duke shook his head. "She picks her spot. She squats. Her foot grips. It locks. That's it. Amazing!"

Once alone, visions of the dragon, the granddaddy of all dragons, lurking in the twilight paraded through Duke's mind. A chill ran through him. Nervously he glanced around. Then, satisfied that he was safe for the time being, he slid down into the leaves. As always, it felt strange and empty not having Prince beside him.

"Stone is hard and stars shine," he murmured, pressing the stone to his chest as if trying to force the idea into his heart. "Things are what they are and people are who they are. What is, is, and what was, was."

As night fell, his thoughts drifted to all the times that day he had broken the law of the land as he struggled to replace his crooked thoughts with straight ones. If only the grace period were longer. He ached with sadness and feared that his heart would never get lighter. He just *had* to take acceptance into his heart and make it part of him. Then he remembered: no *had to's*! He just *wanted* to, really, really *wanted* to—and soon.

He gazed up into the sable sky twinkling with brightly shining stars and realized that the stone was not the only thing that had taken on new meaning. There they were, brilliant specks of wonder in the vast darkness, boldly doing what they were made to do.

"Please," he whispered urgently, "give me the serenity I need to accept the things I can't change."

CHAPTER NINE

An Arresting Development

The next morning after a light breakfast, Duke took an apple and a couple of carrots from the basket and placed them in his satchel. Not wanting crumbs all over his hero tools, he decided against taking any of the leftover biscuits. He struggled to his feet, pulled the satchel over his shoulder, and called to Maxine.

"Oops, I overslept," came the reply. "I'll be right down."

Soon Maxine dropped from the branches in a free fall. Duke held his breath, fearing she would crash to the ground. But at the last moment she threw open her wings like a parachute and fluttered them madly, pulling herself out of the dive. Up, up she went, circling and then gliding gently to the ground.

"Sorry, I didn't mean to scare you," she said, fluffing her feathers. "I couldn't resist. I may have lost the hummingbird competition but I still came out ahead. I learned a great fluttering style, didn't I?"

"That's how you look at it?" he asked. "You came out ahead even though you lost?"

"Yes. No experience is ever wasted if you learn from it."

Duke started out on the path again, Maxine hopping

along beside him. "A lot of my experiences seem like a big waste," Duke lamented, "and I don't want this trip to end up the same way. I won't let it. I've been thinking straight since I got up, even about my son. I accept that he isn't a Johnny. He never was and probably never will be. He's a J-J-Jonathan. There, I said it."

Maxine stopped and stared at him.

"Didn't you hear me?" Duke asked. "What's the matter?"

"What else did you say? To yourself, I mean? Way down deep. The thoughts hidden beneath the thoughts you know you had."

He looked down at the ground and sighed. "Well, I—"

All of a sudden a shrill whistle sounded, once...twice... three times.

"What's that?" he asked.

"Duke, I want to prepare you for—"

"I hear horses' hooves and a wagon! Doc must have found my dragon wagon and sent it to me! I hope Prince is on it. I miss him so much! And he'd be a big help with the dragon when it shows up."

"I don't think—"

"Yes, that must be it! Look. Here it comes!"

"No, Duke—"

"Hey, those aren't my white stallions...and that's not my dragon wagon either."

A black-and-white wagon drawn by a team of black horses raced up to Duke and Maxine and rumbled to a stop. On the side of the wagon were an official-looking gold insignia and the words *Serenity Police Department*. Two officers in black uniforms with big brass buttons and matching black hats jumped out and seized Duke.

One officer said sternly, "Duke the Dragon Slayer, you are under arrest for breaking the law of the land. Anything you say can and will be used against you in a court of law. Please come with us."

"Hey!" shouted Duke, trying to pull his arms free as the officers half-walked, half-dragged him to the wagon. "I'm not going anywhere with you. I didn't do anything! Let go of me! Hey, watch it. You'll knock off my bag! Max, Max, do something!"

"I'll come with you. Right now that's all I can do."

"This isn't fair! I didn't say anything!"

"I told you before, thinking counts," Maxine reminded him as she flew into the wagon.

Duke fussed and fumed as the officers loaded him in and drove off.

"Why am I being punished when I'm just learning?" he asked Maxine as the wagon bumped along the Path of Serenity. "Don't they know I can think straight? I'll prove it. I won't say they can't do this to me, that it's not fair or that it's awful or terrible or anything. I'll say that it's too bad—very too bad—and that I would much prefer—greatly prefer, very, very greatly prefer—that this wasn't happening," he said, clenching his fists until they turned white, his voice growing louder and louder. "See, I can say the right things. Why won't they stop this blankety-blank wagon?"

"Because you are white-knuckling it," said Maxine.

"Why does it matter what color my knuckles are?" Duke asked, exasperated.

"White knuckles show that you haven't accepted what is, that you're forcing yourself to say things you don't believe and are angry about. Since you haven't accepted the things you've been saying, you have disobeyed the law of the land."

"I'm not white-knuckling it! I'm pretending to believe, the way Willie told me to. And what do they do? They arrest me and haul me away like a common criminal!"

"That's one way to view it."

One way to view it. One way to view it. The words whirled around in Duke's mind.

Then he remembered. "STOP, STOP, STOP!" he shouted to his crooked thoughts. He took a deep breath, and another and another, muttering frantically, "What am I supposed to do? Let's see. I have to think about my thinking. Yes, that's it! No wonder I'm so upset. Okay now, okay. Get a grip, Duke. This isn't so awful. It isn't so terrible. I—I can survive this. I can."

"DUKE! DUKE!" yelled Maxine.

"WHAT! WHAT! I'm pretty busy here, Max."

"A little too busy, but you're getting the hang of it."

"Really?"

"Yes. After all, this was your first solo emergency self-rescue. I didn't jump in to help you this time."

"Yeah, that's right, you didn't. Well then, I guess I didn't do so bad. I'm still worried about what's going to happen to me now, though. I've never been arrested in my whole life. Am I going to prison?"

"The only prisons in the Land of Serenity are those that people construct themselves."

"I know a lot about those," Duke said, suddenly feeling sad as he recalled the picture of the imprisoned, crying heart in his book. "Will I have a record?"

"Not a police record," Maxine replied. "Just a record in the annals of time, where all things are recorded."

"I wish I knew why this is happening."

"We don't always know why things happen, but this is part of your journey."

Duke rolled his eyes. "Obviously."

"You've been arrested by the Serenity Police. That's a fact. And there is nothing you can do to change it. You might as well relax and enjoy the scenery."

"And I thought talking to you would make me feel better," he grumbled.

"It's your *own* talk that can make you feel better, Duke, remember?"

"I know, I know," he said with resignation. "Stone is hard and stars shine. I'm trying to see this differently."

"Why don't you try out your New View glasses."

"Do you think it's okay? I thought they were only for fighting the dragon."

"Not all dragons are visible. You can use your tools whenever you need them."

"It's kind of spooky to think there are dragons around that I can't see, but this doesn't seem to be a good time to talk about it," Duke said, fishing around in his satchel until he found the glasses. "I've got enough problems."

He put on the glasses and immediately recalled how he had once felt about the schoolhouse and the ABCs and Willie. "These really work!" he exclaimed, reaching back into the bag and grabbing his stone and straight-thinking stick.

A few minutes later his face brightened. "Is this wagon ride saving us from having to walk all this way?"

"Nice. You're beginning to see a positive side to your latest adversity."

The wagon came to a stop in front of a building made entirely of earth-toned natural stones in various shapes and sizes. They created a pattern unlike any Duke had ever seen. A wide stairway led up to an entrance flanked by stately columns.

"Where are we?" Duke asked in wonder, pulling off his glasses and putting them and the stone and stick back into his satchel.

"We are exactly where you need to be to lighten your heart," Maxine answered.

Before Duke could ask what she meant, the officers took him by the arms and helped him out of the wagon. They walked him to the bottom of the stairs. Maxine flew alongside.

Frowning, Duke surveyed the long stairway. "You'd think that whoever runs this place would know that people with heavy hearts would have trouble climbing all these."

"Duke!" cautioned Maxine.

"I guess I put away my hero tools too soon. I know, the stairs are there and there's nothing I can do about it. I might as well accept it and start climbing."

He started up the stairs, leaving the officers behind. As he made his way to the top he had a frightening thought. "What about the dragon? Is this where I have to slay it? I mean, I'm going to be punished somehow and you said there are no regular prisons—"

"Fighting the dragon that lives on this path is not a punishment. It's a rite of passage," replied Maxine, hovering beside him.

"A what?"

"You'll see."

Duke shook his head. "I hate when you say that."

CHAPTER TEN

The Universe Versus
Duke the Dragon Slayer

At the top of the stairs next to two big entry doors was a sign that read:

SUPREME COURT

OF

THE LAND OF SERENITY

"Court!" Duke sputtered. "I have to stand trial? What are they going to do to me?"

"Nothing compared to what you've already done to yourself," explained Maxine. "Don't worry. I'll be with you."

Realizing there was no use trying to get an answer out of his feathered companion, Duke took a deep breath and pulled open the doors.

The room looked like an ordinary courtroom except that it had no ceiling, which seemed odd. A large gold insignia like the one on the police wagon hung prominently on the far wall. In front of it was a platform that held a massive desk and thronelike chair.

Maxine led Duke through the gallery to a seat in the first row behind a long wooden table.

"Are you going to be my lawyer?" he asked as he sat down.

"No, you are to argue your own case," she answered, landing on his shoulder.

His mind darted from here to there and there to here. He had to think. He had to prepare. But he didn't know what to prepare for or what to think. Then he realized that it probably wouldn't matter what he said. He was guilty, and that's all there was to it.

The door to the judge's chambers swung open, and in came a burly black bear. He lumbered past the platform to the front of the room and stared out over the crowd of two.

He puffed up his chest and called out in a husky voice, "All rise. The Supreme Court of the Land of Serenity in and for the County of Acceptance is now in session. The honorable Merlin the Magician presiding."

Duke couldn't believe what was happening. "Merlin for a judge! A bear for a bailiff! This is ridiculous!"

Maxine hushed him. "Stand up or you'll be held in contempt of court."

Duke scrambled out of his seat—as best a man with a Type II heavy heart, a satchel in his lap, and a bird on his shoulder can—and stood at attention. So did Maxine.

Right on cue, the door opened again and in swept the famous sage Merlin, gray-bearded and wearing a flowing white robe. Squirrels and rabbits and birds surrounded him. With a swoosh of his garment he lowered himself into the grand chair. The animals scampered and scurried and hopped to the gallery seats behind Duke and Maxine, and remained standing.

The bailiff's deep voice rang out again. "All parties having business before this court, please step forward."

"That's us," said Maxine. She pointed at the long wooden table. "Walk over to the defendant's table."

"All remaining parties may be seated," continued the bailiff.

The animals settled into their seats and the room quieted down. The bailiff announced, "The Universe versus Duke the Dragon Slayer."

"The universe versus me! He can't be serious!"

"Shh, shh," Maxine warned. "You know how to handle this. Be quiet and think about your thinking."

As Merlin leafed through the case file, Duke thought about his thinking, straightened it out, and calmed himself down. Suddenly he realized the Merlin he had heard about since childhood was seated right in front of him. Unable to restrain his excitement, he blurted out, "It is indeed an honor to meet Your Honor, Your Honor. And I'm really glad you are my judge. I hope it's okay to say that."

"Thank you, Duke," Merlin said, the slightest hint of a grin peeking through his courtroom demeanor. He cleared his throat. "Please understand that although I am a judge *in* these proceedings, I am not the judge *of* these proceedings, nor do I control the amount of benefit you derive from them. You do. You are your own judge and jury, and you argue your own case, as you do every day of your life." He tapped his gavel. "The proceedings will now begin."

"What proceedings?" Duke whispered to Maxine. "If I'm the only one doing anything here, what kind of proceedings can there be?"

"Shh!" she whispered again. "Accept, don't expect."

Merlin tapped his gavel again. "Duke the Dragon Slayer, you have been charged with breaking the Law of the Land of Serenity. In most courts you would now be asked to enter a plea of guilty or not guilty."

Duke held his breath as Merlin continued. "Fortunately for you and others who appear here, we do not follow this procedure. We are not interested in crime and punishment—although it is a well-known book, and one could argue that it is indeed interesting."

A look of uncertainty crossed the magician's face. "Oh my. Has that been written yet? Hmm . . . well, no matter. The bottom line is that you are here to be helped, not condemned. You may be seated."

Duke exhaled in relief. "Helped to do what, Your Honor?" he asked, grateful to sit down.

Merlin rested his arms on the desk and leaned forward. "Helped to get rid of stubborn old crooked thinking habits and beliefs that keep coming back even when you've tried repeatedly to get rid of them."

"Yes, yes! That's what got me arrested! How did you know? Was it in those papers you were looking at?"

"Yes, it was, and your problem is a common one," Merlin replied. "Even when part of you knows better, another part—an emotional voice deep inside—insists that your old crooked thoughts are true."

"You're right. That's the voice I'm having trouble with."

"I'm sure you are," Merlin said compassionately. "And that voice won't give up until you challenge it with logic and reason."

"Isn't that sort of what I've been doing?"

"You've been substituting straight thoughts for crooked ones. That's fast and easy and is sometimes all that's needed. But some crooked thoughts are so automatic and so stubborn that you need more powerful ammunition to win your battle against them."

That piqued Duke's curiosity. "What kind of ammunition can fight thoughts in your head?"

"A sure-fire test that will prove whether your thoughts are actually true and factual, or are simply opinions that can be changed."

"A test?"

"Yes, one that uses special questions to challenge what you've been telling yourself. It's a very important test. So important, in fact, that it is the D of the ABCs of emotions."

A groan tumbled out before Duke could stop it. "Oh wait, wait," he said, quickly rethinking his thoughts. "If D works as well as the rest of the ABCs, my heart could get lighter real soon. There's one thing, though—test begins with a T, so why is it the D of the ABCs?"

"Because you challenge and test your thoughts by disputing them—and *disputing* begins with D."

"And you already had a C word, right? I learned about that at the schoolhouse. So how do you do it? Dispute, I mean."

"I'll show you," Merlin offered. "Tell me the main crooked thought that got you arrested."

"Are you talking about the problem with my son?"

"I'm talking about the main crooked thought that has you hoodwinked into *believing* you have a problem with him."

"Well, I've tried hard not to believe this, but it seems so true—"

"It's all right, son," Merlin said gently. "That's why you're here. Go ahead and say it."

"Um, if you say so, Your Honor, Merlin Sir." He swallowed hard. "Jonathan *has* to become a dragon slayer."

"Why does he *have* to?" countered Merlin.

"That's a *special* question?"

"Yes, it is. Answer it. You'll see."

Duke shrugged. "Because it's our family tradition."

"Why does he *have* to follow in your family tradition?"

"Because he does. It's the right thing to do."

"How do you know? Where's the proof that it's the right thing?"

"What do you mean, proof? He just *should*. He's meant to, that's all."

"Well then, where is the evidence that he *should*, that he's meant to? Where is it written? What law of the universe commands it?"

"It's not written anywhere. I mean there's no law exactly. But everyone agrees with me. They all expect him to become a dragon slayer too, and to be the best one. After all, he is my son and my father's grandson and my great grandfather's—"

"Even if it were true that everyone agrees, what proof would there be that everyone is right?"

A feeling of uncertainty came over Duke. "I—I don't know. Everyone can't be wrong." He paused. "Well, come to think of it, not every single person thinks he has to become a dragon slayer. *He* doesn't, and neither does his mother." Duke sighed.

"I'm going to ask you again," Merlin said steadily. "If it's true that your son absolutely *should* be, *ought* to be, *has* to be, *must* be, is *supposed* to be, is *meant* to be a dragon slayer, where is the proof?"

"Okay, I give up," Duke replied, exasperated. "I guess there isn't any."

"That's because Jonathan's having to become a dragon slayer is not a fact. It's only an idea in your head—one that he doesn't have to follow. Do you see now that just believing something doesn't make it true?"

"But it seems so obvious," Duke insisted. "I mean it feels so right. I've been thinking about his being a dragon slayer since the moment he was born."

"Crooked thoughts are like that. They can trick you into believing they're facts, and before you know it you're making unrealistic demands that get you into a lot of trouble. You may have always believed that your son should be a rough, tough, dragon-slaying hero, but that's just your opinion—one he and the universe apparently disagree with."

"It's really hard to tell opinions from facts," Duke said. "Crooked thoughts seem so true when you're thinking them."

"Yes, but a fact is a fact. It's logical. It can be proven. You, Duke, may think it's too cold in here. And you, Mister Bailiff, with all your fur, may think it's just fine. These are valid truths for each of you, but they are opinions, not facts. The only fact is that the temperature is sixty-six degrees. You could verify that by using a thermometer."

Duke furrowed his brow. "What's a thermometer?"

"Oh my," Merlin said, flustered. "I suspect I've done it again. Hasn't that been invented yet? Well, never mind. A thermometer is an instrument that gives an objective measurement. It tests the temperature."

Duke thought for a moment. Then his face lit up. "So disputing is a thermometer for thoughts, huh?" He shook his head. "This is really something. All this time I've been telling myself upsetting things that aren't even true."

"Yes, and what has that done for you? Has it gotten you what you want? Has it made you happy, healthy, peaceful? Has it helped to make your life good, full, satisfying?"

"Are you kidding? I mean, no sir, Your Honor sir. It's made me miserable. It's given me a heavy heart and made my life run amok. That's what thinking crooked has done for me."

"Then does it make sense to keep thinking what you have been?"

"Well…no, no it doesn't," Duke answered.

"All right. Then what could you tell yourself instead about your son that would make you feel better and make your life better?"

"Let's see. I have to think about how to word that."

"Fine," Merlin said. He tapped his gavel. "Court will now take a short recess. I suggest, Duke, that you also use this time to digest what we've discussed and to add your new lessons to your book."

The magician rose and disappeared back into his chambers.

Maxine piped up. "Lessons aren't *all* there is to digest around here." She pointed with her wing. "Look."

Duke turned and saw two yellow warblers helping several rabbits and squirrels who were scurrying to set out an assortment of nuts and seeds and berries. Although he had serious concerns about the catering service's adherence to basic hygiene, he dismissed the thought and eagerly partook of the refreshments. Maxine did too, but of course she was used to that style of eating.

Nibbling on some nuts, Duke returned to his seat and reached into his satchel for his book and pen. He thought about what he had learned and made notes on truth, facts, and opinions. With Maxine's help he wrote:

LESSON #3

DISPUTING: *D* OF THE ABCs

MY THERMOMETER FOR THOUGHTS

Test stubborn, upsetting thoughts by asking special questions:

1. *Is my thought true? Why? How do I know? Is it logical? Where is the proof, the evidence?*

2. *How does thinking this make me feel? Does it make me happy, healthy, peaceful?*

3. *How is thinking this working for me in my life? Is it getting me what I want? Is it helping to make my life good, full, satisfying?*

4. *Does it make sense to keep thinking this? If not, what could I think instead that would work better for me?*

Next, he worked on coming up with some new straight thoughts about Jonathan. It wasn't easy to do with the old voice in his head insisting they weren't true, but he persisted. When he finished, he leaned back in his chair and closed his eyes, his mind as full as his stomach. Visions of the stone walls reminded him that what was, was, and what is, is.

The chatter around Duke faded into the distance, and for the moment peace was his.

CHAPTER ELEVEN

The Battle of Acceptance County

"All rise," commanded the bailiff. Everyone in the court room scrambled to their feet.

With a swish of his robe, Merlin swept back into the courtroom and took his seat. The bailiff said, "You may be seated. Court is now back in session. The case of the Universe versus Duke the Dragon Slayer will now resume."

Merlin observed Duke for a moment before speaking. "You look as if something is bothering you, Duke. What is it?"

"If I tell you, will we have to dispute again?"

"We don't *have* to but it might be preferable."

"With all due respect, Your Honor, you're really into this stuff, aren't you?" Duke began. "I guess I'd better be also because that voice in my head was at it again when I was writing down my new lessons. It kept insisting that this is all just a bunch of mumbo jumbo and that it *would* be awful if my son didn't become a dragon slayer. And it told me I'm kidding myself if I think I'd be able to stand it. So even though I know better, it still *feels* like it would be awful."

Merlin nodded. "That's not unusual," he said reassuringly. "Remember, it takes time and practice to change old thinking habits. And it takes even longer for what you *know* to become what you *feel*. Emotions are slow that way. Just keep disputing, Duke, and your new way of thinking and feeling will eventually sink in."

"That sounds like it could take awhile. In the meantime, it still seems like it would be awful."

"Why would it be awful?"

"Because . . . because I wouldn't like it."

"That would make it too bad and disappointing. But how does that prove it's awful?"

"I don't know exactly," Duke said, a bit irritated. "It would be, that's all."

"There's no proof, though, no evidence, isn't that correct?"

Duke hesitated. "Well, yeah, it's not written anywhere and it's not a law of the universe and it's not a fact, but it still seems like it would be awful."

"How is it making you feel to keep telling yourself that?"

"Awful. When I *think* about it being awful, it *feels* awful. It still feels true, though."

Suddenly Merlin slapped his hand on the desk. "You know, Duke, on second thought, I think you're right. It would indeed be awful, and no doubt terrible and horrible. Probably even worse than that. In fact it would be the worst thing I can think of! The absolute worst! Worse than the world falling off its axis. Worse than being caught in a glacier without a hot water bottle. Worse than someone inventing a mechanical dragon-slaying machine. I don't see how you could possibly survive it. It's so-o-o-o ter-r-r-r-rible I can barely *stand* to talk about it." He pretended to struggle to his feet, then dropped back into his chair. "Oh, no! I can't stand to *sit* talking about it either. Change the subject—quick!"

Duke was stunned. He shot a quizzical look at Maxine and then back at Merlin.

"I'll give you a hint," offered Maxine. She flew down and yanked Duke's pant leg with her beak.

"Hey, quit it, Max," he barked, trying to pull away.

"Oh, so it's okay for Merlin to pull your leg but not me?" she teased.

Sounds of muffled laughter rose from the gallery. Duke looked behind him and saw rows of squirming animals with an assortment of paws and wings over their mouths. When he turned back around, Merlin had a grin and a playful look of satisfaction on his face. Maxine was straining to hold back a giggle. Even the bailiff had a paw over his mouth to hide a smile that threatened to crack through his tough exterior.

Anticipation hung in the air like ripe fruit ready to fall from a tree. Duke wasn't sure what to make of it.

Unable to contain himself another moment, the bailiff began to guffaw. Duke, suddenly realizing what was happening, burst into laughter too. So did everyone else. The entire gallery hopped around gaily in their seats. Maxine giggled harder and harder, rolling around on the table, holding her sides with her wings, until finally she rolled right off.

That's just like her, Duke thought. *I wonder how often she does this.*

The bailiff, still in the throes of laughter, tried to get all of them quieted down. "Order in the court. Order in the court," he choked out between guffaws. Everyone started laughing even harder. Finally Merlin tapped his gavel. When the clamor settled, he asked Duke how he was feeling.

"Better. Lightening up has its advantages," Duke answered, winking at Maxine, "but I hope my crooked-thinking voice doesn't keep coming back and trying to change my mind."

"It probably will," Merlin replied. "That voice has had a long reign of thinking it is ruler of the universe. You're challenging its power, so it's no surprise that it's putting up the fight of its life. But you can win this battle, as you have numerous others, if you keep arguing with the voice in your head that's trying to keep you thinking the old way."

Duke sighed at the thought.

"This may be the biggest battle of your life," Merlin continued, his voice increasing in intensity. "But it will result in the biggest rewards. If you are to take control of your heart and your life, you need your new view—your new thoughts—to be victorious. As a dragon slayer, you know about being victorious. Fight to the death! To the death of your old view, your old thoughts!"

But Merlin's rousing battle cry didn't rouse Duke. A look of defeat crept over the dragon slayer's face. "There was a time when I would have looked forward to a good battle. Not anymore. Now I'm so tired. My life seems like it's been one battle after another—to live up to my father's and grandfather's reputations, to be the best dragon-slaying student, the number one dragon slayer, and everyone's hero. I battled dragon after dragon to keep my title, and even battled my own son to get him to follow in the family tradition. It's still a battle to drag around this heavy heart. And now, after all that, not only do I have a new dragon to fight on this path, but I have to fight *myself* too. I just don't know if I have enough strength left to do it."

He crossed his arms on the table and buried his face in them.

Merlin stepped down from the platform and went over to Duke. He gently placed his hand on the dragon slayer's shoulder. "Fighting life's inevitable battles as if they are all a matter of life and death would exhaust anyone. Most people who come before this court are battle weary. But they are the ones who can benefit most from engaging in this battle of all battles against their crooked thinking. For it is the one battle that can make all others easier, both those still being fought and those yet to come."

"I don't know. I don't know," Duke moaned in a muffled voice.

"You are already learning how to think differently about the battles in your life. When reason prevails, they won't be the draining ordeals they have been. And, happily, not all crooked thoughts require long and arduous fights. Some give up without much struggle. Many people as worn out as you have succeeded."

Duke raised his head. "Really?"

"Yes," answered Merlin, sitting down on the edge of the table, "and they had the same choice you do—to turn back and become one more set of footprints retreating, or to march onward to victory, to serenity and lightheartedness."

To Duke, serenity and lightheartedness seemed so far away. "Are you sure that if I keep fighting my crooked thinking I'll be able to follow the law of the land and accept the things I can't change?"

Merlin nodded.

Duke looked at Maxine thoughtfully, then back at Merlin. Pushing against the weight of his heavy heart, he struggled to his feet. He glanced at Maxine again before turning to address the gallery.

"A bird once told me that doing what seems easier at first is often harder in the long run, or something like that. I've come too far to turn back now. Besides, I've never walked away from a battle yet, although I did *run* away from one—but there were extenuating circumstances. Anyway, I came on this journey to find serenity and it doesn't look like I'm going to find it with my old crooked thinking. I really need to get rid of this heavy heart, and I'm still determined to do it."

Merlin was pleased. "Good decision, Duke."

The animals in the gallery erupted into chirps and squeals and cheers. The bailiff thrust his fist into the air. "Yea, Duke. On to victory!"

"When will I be ready to go?" Duke asked.

"When your disputing has helped you create a healthy new philosophy about Jonathan, an effective straight-thinking philosophy. That's the E of the ABCs."

"E, huh? May I have a moment, Your Honor?"

"Certainly. Take your time."

"Thank you. And, Your Honor, sir, I—I have one more request. Could I pace and crack just a little? I—I really need to. I do my best thinking that way."

Merlin smiled. "Of course."

Duke rose and began pacing and cracking—and mumbling. Back and forth he went—crack, mumble, mumble, crack. He stopped and conferred with Maxine, then back and forth he went again—crack, mumble, mumble, crack.

Finally he stopped in front of Merlin. "Okay, Your Honor. I think I have a philosophy that might work. Here goes. There's no reason why Jonathan *has to* become a dragon slayer, although I would prefer it. I *want* him to but I don't *need* him to. The idea that he *has to* isn't written anywhere. It's not a law of the universe. It's only a rule in my head that he doesn't have to follow. There's no proof, so it isn't true. It's not a fact." Duke paused. "That's the first part. How am I doing so far?"

Merlin gave him a thumbs-up.

"Whew! Now I'll do the next part. Continuing to believe he has to be a dragon slayer will only hurt me more. It won't get him to do it because he is who he is, and it will keep upsetting me so much that I'll never find serenity or get rid of my heavy heart."

He took a deep breath and went on. The courtroom was

silent as the animals hung on his every word. "I hope this isn't getting too long, but there's one more important part. If Jonathan doesn't become a dragon slayer it will be too bad, very too bad, but it won't be awful or terrible or anything exaggerated like that, and I'll be able to stand it without white-knuckling it, so I won't get arrested anymore. How's that?" he asked proudly.

Merlin stood up and shook Duke's hand. "Congratulations, Duke. It sounds as if you've been thinking straight all your life. Now remember to keep thinking this way when your crooked thoughts creep back. It appears there is no need to remand you to Maxine's custody, although she is still to accompany you. You are free to go."

A resounding applause exploded from the gallery.

"Thank you, Your Honor," Duke said gratefully, pumping Merlin's hand up and down. "It's been a real honor, Your Honor, having the great Merlin the Magician help me set my thinking straight. I can't wait to tell the guys at the Hero Shoppe about meeting you, if I ever have the nerve to go back there, that is."

"You will if you keep doing what you've been doing. Knowing one can handle whatever adversity arises gives one fortitude heretofore unimagined," Merlin advised.

"I'll take your word for it," Duke said with a smile. He picked up his satchel, slung it over one shoulder, and offered Maxine a seat on the other. Then he looked up above him. "I've been curious about something, Your Honor, but I haven't had time to ask. Is there any particular reason why this court-room has no ceiling?"

"Oh, that's so when we have night court the stars will shine down and remind people about what is and what was. In the daylight, of course, the stone building serves that purpose."

Duke nodded. "Night court. Hmm, clever." He turned toward the entrance, then toward the side door, not sure which way to go.

Suddenly another door appeared and swung wide open. A sign above it read:

WAY TO GO, DUKE!

He grinned and marched to the door, waving his hand in the air, forming two fingers into a V for victory.

CHAPTER TWELVE

The Mystery of the O Well

As Duke continued along the path, deep in thought, Maxine flew from tree to bush to tree, keeping pace and taking in the scenery.

"You're unusually quiet," she said after some time.

"I've been practicing. Fighting my crooked thoughts is harder than fighting dragons, but it's getting easier. Everything I've learned is falling into place."

"And it will get even easier. Before you know it, thinking straight will become a habit the same way thinking crooked did."

Duke continued practicing until Maxine asked, "Do you want to play a game?"

"I'm pretty busy, Max. What kind of game?"

"It's called *What If.*"

"I know that game. You ask yourself stuff like, what if the sky falls in?"

"That's the version most people know, but this one is different. In this one, you imagine you believe differently than you do about something, and you see how that makes you feel. Here, I'll show you. What if you believed that Jonathan is a fascinating young man who, because he is unlike you, can bring some interesting new things into your life and that you like him as he is? Can you imagine that? What would happen?"

"That's a heck of a way to test out a new view," Duke replied with mock sarcasm. "It's sort of like Willie's pretending and acting *as if*."

"That's the idea," she encouraged. "It really works. Try it."

Duke turned the new view over and over in his mind.

"It's odd," he finally said. "I've been concentrating so hard on not thinking it's awful that my son is different from me that it never occurred to me there might be a good side to it. If I believed what you said, I would be happy and be able to appreciate Jonathan. Now I see why Merlin said I only *thought* I had a problem with him. There's nothing wrong with him. My crooked thinking was the problem!"

Maxine hopped up and down with excitement. "Yes! And what if you believed that all your relationships have been valuable teachers and that they helped to set you off on this adventurous path that you otherwise might not have traveled, learning things you've needed to learn all your life? When one door closes, another opens, you know."

"Valuable teachers and open doors. Hmm." The truth trickled through Duke's mind, leaving specks of peace in its wake.

Satisfied that Duke had plenty to contemplate, Maxine flew ahead, taking another little tour of the countryside.

It all made perfect sense to Duke now. He disputed one crooked thought after another, winning the battle with some and stubbornly chipping away at others.

Wait a minute, he thought. *That's just my opinion. I could be right. I could be wrong. I can change my mind and take a new view.* And again and again he did. He made up new straight thoughts and repeated each one, reminding himself that his old way of thinking didn't work, that it had done nothing but bury him in problems. He used everything he had learned to help him accept the things he couldn't change. Gradually, his voice of reason grew stronger, and his crooked-thinking voice grew weaker.

Suddenly he felt an odd sensation in his chest. He thought his heart felt a tiny bit lighter. "Max! Max! Come quick!" he called out.

Maxine returned using her fastest hummingbird flutter. "What is it, Duke? Are you okay?" she gasped, out of breath.

"It's my heart, Max! Could it be getting lighter?"

"Oh, *that*," she answered, relieved. "Of course. That's the point of doing what you've been doing, isn't it? You've been accepting things you can't change, and voilà—your heart is getting lighter, as promised."

Duke was beside himself with joy. "It's working! It's happening right now as I'm talking to you! It's only a little, but I can definitely feel it. Doc was right!"

His lighter heart made walking easier, and Duke picked up the pace. Soon they came upon an old well at the side of the path. A sign on it read:

O WELL

Glad to have found water, Duke hurried over to the well, grabbed the rope, and lowered the bucket.

"That isn't just any old water, Duke," warned Maxine.

"I don't care as long as it's safe to drink."

"Oh, it's a lot more than just safe."

"What do you mean a lot more?" he asked, pulling the bucket back up and filling the metal cup that was attached to it.

"Drink some and see for yourself," she replied.

The liquid looked like ordinary water and tasted like ordinary water. But after a few sips Duke began to feel rather strange. He peered into the cup. "Hey, what is this stuff?"

"How are you feeling?" Maxine asked, restraining her excitement.

"Relaxed in a funny sort of way. Tell me the truth, Max. Is there any juice in this stuff?"

"No, it's just O Well water—honest."

"What's that?"

"I'll give you a hint," she said with a twinkle in her eye.

"Okay, but watch it. The last hint you gave me nearly ripped my pants."

Sure enough, Maxine flew down and yanked on his pant leg with her beak.

Duke started to object, then changed his mind. *Oh well,* he thought, *there goes Max again, being Max, teaching me stuff in her way. But what's the big deal? My pants probably won't rip, and if they do, so what? They're only pants.*

Startled by his own reaction, he said aloud, "I can't believe this! What's going on?"

Maxine jumped into the air, threw open her wings, and yelled, "Surprise! The O Well water is a hero tool! It helps you say 'oh well' to things that aren't easy to say 'oh well' to. It works great for crooked thinking."

"A hero tool! O Well—that's it?"

"Yes, nothing complicated. Simply oh well. When things don't go your way and you know you can't change them, the O Well water helps you say to yourself, 'Oh well. That's the way it goes sometimes. There's nothing I can do about it.' It makes it easier to accept it and move on. Isn't that wonderful?"

"It would be if it really works on hard things like the stubborn thoughts I'm still having trouble with."

"Go ahead. Take another sip and give it a real test."

So Duke did. And somehow the O Well water seemed to wash away every stubborn thought that paraded through his mind.

"Amazing! You ever think about selling this stuff?"

Maxine smiled. "Everyone who's tried it says the same thing, but it doesn't work that way. It's meant for people on this journey. Why don't you fill your canteen so you'll have some for later. It'll help get you through the rest of this land without breaking the law again."

"Do you know something I don't? What's going to happen? And please, Max, don't tell me I'll find out in good time or that I'll see."

"Okay, I won't," she said, pretending to zip her mouth closed with her wing.

Duke took another sip of the O Well water and shrugged. "Oh well," he said in a melodious tone. "Maybe I'm better off not knowing what's next. Whatever will be, will be. Hmm, that would make a good song title. Let's see, I need a melody." He hummed a few bars. "Hey," he said, holding up the cup, "this stuff is really getting to me! I'm writing songs like Doc. How does this funny water work, anyway?"

"It's a mystery," Maxine replied, her eyes widening. "A magical kind of mystery."

Duke shrugged again. "Oh well, I don't have to know."

He opened his satchel and took out the canteen. After filling it with water, he put it back into his satchel, and he and Maxine set out again on the path.

CHAPTER THIRTEEN

The Showdown

With his new loyal companion accompanying him, Duke continued along the often difficult Path of Serenity, maneuvering around brambly brush and potholes, over rocks, and past boulders that stood in his way.

Excited at the prospect of lightening his heart, he worked harder than ever to accept the things he could not change. From time to time he checked with Maxine to find out whether or not a particular thing could be changed. Figuring out what could be from what could not wasn't always as obvious as it seemed, and he didn't want to make any mistakes.

Just as he thought he was winning the fight to accept all that had happened with Allie and Jonathan and Cindy, old battles he was still fighting deep inside started popping into his mind. They were battles he had hardly known were still waging until they had tumbled out of his mouth back at the courthouse.

With Maxine's help he rethought his thoughts, straightening them out and disputing stubborn ones, determined to accept the pain of his past. As the voice of reason wandered through his memories, it rewove the tapestry of his life.

That's when it happened—again.

This time it was unmistakable. His chest lifted. He could stand straighter and it became easier to keep from toppling forward. "Max! Max!" he called out, putting his hand to his chest. "My heart! My heart! It's getting lighter again!"

"I know! I know!" she answered with glee.

Feeling prepared for whatever might come and eager to meet it, Duke asked, "Are we going to get to the next land soon? I think I've done all I need to here. I'm living by the Law of the Land of Serenity, really, truly living by it. My lighter heart is proof of that."

He threw open his arms and proclaimed, "I completely accept the things I can't change, and this time I know what I'm talking about! I feel the acceptance way down inside and I will live it from this day forward. I vow that any crooked thought that dares to get in the way will come to a dismal end. Its defeat will be one of my greatest victories. Nothing can stop me now!"

He loved the sound of those words. They made him feel invincible. As he walked he chanted, "Nothing can stop me now! Nothing can stop me now!"

"Except me," said a low, gravelly voice.

Startled, Duke turned and found himself staring up the scaly legs of a gigantic, fierce-looking dragon.

"Who are you?" he asked, his heart thumping wildly.

"Why, the Dragon of Crooked Thinking, of course. I would have thought you'd recognize me by now."

"Your voice does sound familiar," Duke replied.

"It should," the dragon snapped. "You've heard me in your head millions of times."

"But—but I've never seen you before."

"I showed up in person this time so you'd see I mean business. If you know what's good for you, you'll heed this warning." The dragon lowered his head and glared at Duke. "Stop arguing with me all the time or I'll fry your hide!" he snorted, sputtering out a few tired-looking flames.

Duke was astonished and somewhat relieved. He had never seen a dragon with so little firepower. "You're the grand-daddy of all dragons? The one I've been dreading all this time? What happened to you?"

"It's your fault," hissed the dragon. "All your arguing and looking for truth and proof and results and that new view nonsense is sapping the life out of me. But it's going to stop right now, do you hear me?"

Duke called to Maxine, who was flying in a holding pat-tern overhead. "Max! Max, it works! Look how weak the Dragon of Crooked Thinking is! He can hardly throw any flames. Even his voice is weak."

"A temporary setback at most," the dragon retorted angrily. "I'm still bigger than you and I know better than you how things should and should not be. I've changed your mind lots of times and I'm here to do it again—this time for good!"

Duke wagged his finger at the dragon. "No you won't. Not this time or anytime."

"You've always listened to me before," the dragon insisted, slapping his tail.

"Sure, and look where it's gotten me!"

"Don't start with all that stupid results stuff. You're going to end up listening to me. You always do. That's the way it's meant to be."

"How do you know? Where's the proof?" Duke asked.

"I don't have to prove anything to you. You're the one hung up on proving everything. I'm in charge here and you have to listen to me!"

"Oh yeah? Why? Where's the evidence?" Duke demanded. He didn't wait for an answer. "There isn't any and you know it. It's only your opinion. You've had lots of opinions that have gotten me into trouble, like Jonathan has to be a dragon slayer for instance. But that's over. I've already won by proving he doesn't have to, and that it wouldn't be awful and I could stand it just fine!"

"You think so?" sneered the dragon. "Okay, smarty pants. Picture yourself at the Hero Shoppe, sitting at the juice bar with your big-shot hero friends, hearing all about their heroic sons and trying to explain why *your* son does nothing more manly than moving a chess piece, and why he doesn't care enough about you or your family tradition to follow in your footsteps. You can tell yourself all you want that it won't bother you, but it will. When it happens you'll see I was right!"

The image shook Duke to the core. He tried to think about his thinking but it was muddled, and the dragon kept uttering a steady stream of crooked thoughts, making it hard to concentrate. Even though he knew better than to believe anything the dragon said, something inside him began to waver. The best he could do was stand there, stammering objections while trying to get his reasoning back into high gear.

The dragon, taking full advantage of Duke's sudden vulnerability, pounded him with crooked thoughts about Allie and Cindy. Duke tried with all his might to get the dragon to stop, but it was harder to defeat him face to face. Seeing the beast in action was unnerving. And the more unnerved Duke became, the less he argued, and the louder and stronger the dragon's voice grew, and the bigger his flames grew.

Duke's stomach churned and his throat tightened. Desperate to regain control, he took a deep breath and stuck his hand out in front of him. "STOP!" he yelled. But the dragon went on and on, spewing forth his crooked thoughts so strongly and convincingly that they overtook all reason.

Frantically Duke covered his ears. "STOP IT! STOP IT!" he shouted. "I CAN'T STAND ANY MORE!"

"Now you're coming to your senses," the creature said triumphantly.

"Leave me alone!"

"Never," the dragon replied in a booming voice that shook the ground beneath Duke's feet.

Duke knew what was coming but felt helpless to stop it. Sure enough, his heart suddenly became heavier. He panicked and called to Maxine. She was nowhere in sight. Shocked that she had deserted him, he yelled for Doc. The Wise One didn't answer either.

"It's just you and me," the dragon said menacingly.

The air bristled with the unmistakable energy that comes immediately before the final lunge on any dragon-slaying mission. Duke had felt it hundreds of times.

This time was different. This time he was the prey.

The dragon's eyes flashed with fury. "The next time you dare to try shutting me up with your mumbo jumbo, you had better remember *this*!" And with a deafening snort, the beast shot gigantic crackling flames in Duke's direction.

Duke automatically reached for his sword, but of course it wasn't there. He really could have used his fire-retardant dragon-slaying attire about then too. "How could I have come on a mission without my hero tools?" he berated himself, leaping this way and that to dodge the flames dancing around him.

At that moment the satchel slipped from his shoulder and dangled from his arm, knocking him off balance. "My new hero tools! Of course! How could I have forgotten?"

With a surge of newfound energy, Duke grabbed on to the satchel and ran for cover down the path. He ducked behind a bush and crouched, hurriedly rummaging through the hero tools.

Great balls of fire began exploding around him. Startled, Duke looked up. The dragon was sneering down at him.

"How did you sneak up behind me so fast without my hearing you?" Duke asked, wondering why he was making polite conversation with a beast that was about to set him ablaze.

"I've been sneaking up on you for years," the dragon thundered. "It's one of my best tricks."

"So I've noticed," Duke replied. "But I've got some tricks of my own!"

"You mean that pile of junk you call hero tools?" The dragon threw back his head and laughed. "They don't scare me. They don't even work unless you work them, and you're too weak."

"No I'm not, and yes they do. Besides, they're really special—almost magical."

"Yeah, they're a really big deal. If I had boots on I'd be shaking in them."

The dragon might not have been shaking but Duke certainly was—enough for both of them. Doubts raced through his mind. Could Doc be right? Could the new hero tools really help him defeat the dragon?

Figuring he needed all the help he could get, he dumped out the contents of the satchel on the ground. The mere sight of his lesson book resurrected all that he had written inside. He put on the glasses. Instantly his new views about Allie and Jonathan and Cindy became crystal clear. He picked up the stick. His crooked thinking immediately straightened out. Astounded at what was happening, he quickly opened the canteen and took a swig of O Well water and was overcome by the same sense of calm he had felt at the O Well.

A feeling of power swelled inside him.

"So," said the dragon sarcastically, "are you planning to knock me out with that stone and tie me up with that measuring tape, or are you going to force me into submission with that . . . that stick? Oh, and look at those mittens. Nice touch. Are they supposed to keep you from leaving fingerprints at the crime scene? What other lethal weapons have you got there? As if I really care!" He threw back his head and laughed again, this time in great bursts, spewing giant flames into the air.

Duke stood up tall and stared boldly into the dragon's eyes. The dragon stared back without flinching. After a tense moment of squaring off, Duke launched the strongest attack of straight thinking ever, using his best ammunition about Allie and Jonathan and Cindy.

The dragon shot back tremendous streams of crooked thinking in his most intimidating voice, punctuating important points by spewing more giant flames here and there.

But Duke was in rare form. His assault was relentless. One by one he challenged and shot down the dragon's crooked thoughts. With each defeat the dragon grew weaker and smaller, and Duke's heart grew lighter. And the lighter it grew, the harder he fought.

The dragon tried to distract Duke by shooting flames around him, but the flames were so small that Duke merely extinguished them with his boot. Knowing he was losing the battle, the dragon tried a new attack plan—direct assault. "You can't hurt me," he said, his voice cracking. "You're nothing without me. I'm the strongest part of you."

"Not anymore," Duke replied confidently. "*I'm* the strongest part. I have truth on my side. That's why you're getting weaker and smaller. Can't you feel it? Look at your flames. Listen to your voice."

The dragon made one last supreme effort to fight. This time his voice came out in a whisper and his flames were nothing more than sparks.

"You might as well give up," Duke advised. "You're through playing ruler of the universe, dictating what should and should not be, what's meant to be, has to be, making things seem awful and terrible. You don't always know what's best or right. You don't have the wisdom or the power to run the universe. No one does. Haven't you learned that by now?"

"Sure," the dragon remarked. "I've learned you're not quite the pushover you used to be. It doesn't matter. I'll still beat you in the end. You might have won this battle but you haven't won the war. You'll slip up, and besides, other things will happen and I'll be back, stronger than ever!"

The thought made Duke's mouth go dry. He took another sip of O Well water.

"Oh well," he found himself saying, "whatever will be, will be. If you come back, you come back."

"You'll sing a different tune when I show up and catch you off guard next time. I'll be all rested up. Nothing will save you then."

Duke set down the canteen and picked up the sparkling stone lying on the ground. He squeezed it in his hand. It felt cool and reassuring.

"It's the nature of stone to be hard," he said, "and the nature of stars to shine. It's your nature to think crooked and to keep coming back, trying again and again to make me see things your way. And you'll go right on doing it about one thing or another, no matter what. I can't change your nature or completely change your way of expressing it, but listen very carefully to this, Dragon—I can and will be in charge of the effect you have on me!"

The dragon was as furious as he was helpless. "You won't get away with this!" he said in a strained whisper. "Next time I'll beat you for sure! You can count on it!"

"I'll be ready."

By this time the dragon was so weak that it took him three tries to disappear.

"I've won!" Duke shouted. "Victory is mine!"

Suddenly a great burden lifted from him and floated up into the sky. With it went chunks of heaviness from his heart. He looked up, his eyes moist with tears of joy.

"Thank you, thank you," he murmured, "for helping me accept the things I can't change—and for my new hero tools!"

CHAPTER FOURTEEN

The Land of Courage

Banjo music was ringing out everywhere. Duke looked around but no one was in sight.

"Yoo-hoo! Over here," Maxine called out, waving a wing in the air. She was perched on a sign. Doc was beside her, wearing his straw hat and strumming a happy tune on his banjo.

"Where were you?" Duke asked over the music. "I was calling for you—both of you. Did you see? Did you see what I did?"

Doc answered by bursting into song, and Maxine chirped in harmony.

> *Yes, we saw,*
> *We watched in awe,*
> *As you clobbered the granddaddy of dragons.*
> *With tools of a hero*
> *You reduced him to zero—*

"Well, almost," Doc said, interrupting his song to set the record straight.

"Is there more? Go on!" Duke said.

"No need," Doc replied. "You get the idea."

Maxine chimed in. "We're sitting on another idea for you, Duke, literally!"

Duke's gaze fell to the words on the sign below his feathery friends. It said:

WELCOME

TO

THE LAND OF COURAGE

LAW OF THE LAND
Change the things you can.

"Wow!" Duke exclaimed. "I didn't even notice! It's the Land of Courage! I made it to the Land of Courage!"

He hadn't felt this good in a long time. He had defeated the Dragon of Crooked Thinking. His heart was lighter. And now entering the next land would put him even closer to the lasting serenity that would help him get his life back.

Caught up in thoughts about his new adventure, he read the law of the land several times. "Change the things you can. Hmm, let's see. There have been so many things I can't change."

"And some that you can and did," added Doc, giving the kind of hint that didn't put a guy's pant leg in jeopardy.

"I did already? Oh yeah! I changed my views and my thoughts. And I changed my crooked thinking and my heavy heart. That all counts, right? Even though I did it before I got here?"

"Absolutely," Doc said. "You changed some things that needed to be changed and could be. That is what this law is all about."

"Will I get arrested in this land if I don't change something that I can that needs changing?"

"What would be arrested is your progress on the Path of Serenity."

"That wouldn't be so good, but at least I won't be whisked off to another courtroom by the police."

Duke gathered up his hero tools and put them back into the satchel. "I guess it wouldn't do any good to ask you two what's going to happen next."

"Good guess," Doc answered.

Just then a pigeon glided down, landed beside Duke, and danced around on one leg to a cha-cha beat—hop, hop, hop-hop-hop—shaking its other leg toward Duke.

"Sebastian! *Hola! Hola!* You found me!" Duke glanced quizzically at Doc and Maxine but got no reaction. He removed the message from Sebastian's leg. "*Gracias, mi amigo*," he said, waving a quick good-bye as the pigeon flew off. He unrolled the paper and read:

Kingdom Association of Dragon Slayers

Notification of Change in Status
and
Possible Disciplinary Action

To Duke the Dragon Slayer:

This is to inform you that you have lost your standing as Number One Dragon Slayer in the Land.

By unanimous vote of the board, Jock the Dragon Slayer has been selected as your successor, based on his consistently outstanding performance in the number two position.

Furthermore, disciplinary action against you is being considered for the following alleged infractions of the Dragon Slayers' code of ethics:

1. Running from a dragon while on a mission
2. Leaving a lethal weapon unattended (special sword)
3. Reckless driving, endangering trusty sidekick and horses
4. Abandonment of trusty sidekick, horses, dragon wagon, and hero tools
5. Abuse of kingdom property (oak tree)
6. Disappearance without submission of a change of address form

Very truly yours,
The Board of Directors

Duke was so stunned he could hardly breathe. He reread the message in disbelief. Then he crumbled to the ground and wailed like a wounded animal. And he moaned. And he wailed some more, oblivious to everything except the thought that his life was totally ruined forever. He was nothing, a nobody—a humiliatingly disgraced nobody—and he would rather die than have to face everyone who knew.

Disapproving, mocking faces floated before his eyes. Faces of the association's board of directors, of the disciplinary board, of the other members of the association who had looked up to him, and of Jock, the kid who had taken his title. Faces of the guys at the Hero Shoppe and of Jonathan and Allie. And faces of the villagers—dozens, hundreds of them—who used to line the streets cheering as he raced by.

Suddenly he heard voices in the distance wailing over his wailing and moaning over his moaning. Annoyed, he tried to ignore them but couldn't. "What is that?"

"Your new neighbors, if you keep this up," Maxine answered.

"What are you talking about?"

"We'll show you," Doc said as he and Maxine flew over to help Duke stand up. "We are going to take a little detour."

"A detour?" he whined. "I can't. I can't get up. I can't go anywhere. Not now."

"Sure you can. Come on," Maxine said gently, trying to lift him by pulling on his sleeve with her beak. "You can wail and moan along the way, if that's all you can think of to do."

Doc quickly packed up his banjo and hat. He flew ahead of Duke and Maxine, leading them past a detour sign that took them off the Path of Serenity and onto a dusty, barren winding road.

As they traveled along Duke tried to calm himself down by taking deep breaths, but they resulted in nothing more than coughing fits from the dust. And he stopped several times to stick his hand out and shout "Stop!" which was followed each time by some unintelligible muttering. Soon he gave up trying to change his crooked thinking and plunged into a dark silence.

After leaving him to his thoughts for a while Maxine asked, "What are you going to do?"

"Nothing," Duke mumbled. "There's nothing I *can* do."

"What about all you've learned?"

"I learned that the past has passed. It's over. I blew it. And don't remind me about accepting the things I can't change. My life is totally ruined and I can't do a thing about it. I'm guilty of everything I'm accused of and my title is already gone. Everything is gone. Everything I loved. Everything I was. Everyone I cared about and everyone who cared about me. I'm nothing. I'm a nobody. I'm even worse than a nobody. I'm a pathetic old has-been. A pathetic old stupid has-been. Yes, stupid, that's what I am. I did it all to myself! I can't accept that! I can't accept any of it. I can't! I can't!"

Talking about it made the horror so big and so real that

Duke began wailing and moaning again. And his heart began to get heavier.

"What about your hero tools?" Maxine persisted.

"Even *they* can't fix this."

He would have been relieved to simply sink back onto the ground and lie there like a pile of yesterday's trash, but Doc and Maxine urged him on.

As they got closer to the wailing and moaning they could hear yelling too. It grew louder and louder until finally they rounded a bend, and there, under a dark, cloudy sky, was the source of the tortured voices.

Dozens and dozens of people were congregated inside a black picket fence that extended back as far as they could see. A dismal gray banner hung between two trees flanking the front gate:

Bleaksville Community Park

Some people were standing in small groups; others were wandering around. Some were sitting in patio chairs. Others were stretched out on lounges, curled up in hammocks, or partaking of the food and drink on wooden picnic tables. Almost everyone was wailing or moaning or yelling or whining, or some combination of these. Those who weren't were sulking, scowls on their faces and a distant look in their eyes, as if they were wailing and moaning and yelling and whining on the inside.

"What's going on here?" Duke asked over the commotion.

"A self-pity party," Doc answered.

"What's that?"

"Just what it seems. A group of heavy-hearted, self-pitying people sharing their misery with like-minded others. Of course not all the residents of Bleaksville are here. Some are attending individual pity parties, which are ongoing, and some have pretty much taken to their beds, their contributions muffled by their pillows. Then there are those who suffer in silence. Oh, and then there are the people who have made themselves sick and gone to the Bleaksville County Medical Center. If the entire community were to fully participate, the aggregate noise level would be so high on the decibel scale that it would be deafening."

Duke walked closer and put down his satchel. "I've never seen anything like this," he remarked, scanning the unbelievable scene before him, trying to take it all in. Finally he asked, "What are those people doing over there at those wheels? They aren't spinning anything."

"Yes they are," Doc said. "They are spinning their wheels. That is what they all do, whether or not they are actually sitting in front of a wheel. It is the favorite community pastime. They like it better than Ping-Pong, which they found too lively for their taste."

"They must have *some* fun. There's a fire pit over there."

"Yes," Maxine said, "so they can sit around all warm and toasty and wail all night long. Sometimes they play the popular Bleaksville game of who can be the angriest about their anger and the most depressed about their depression. And often they have contests and award prizes to the best awfulizers and terribilizers."

Duke gazed at the miserable mass of humanity. Shoulders drooped, faces drooped, and eyes were dull and lifeless.

"They look like I feel," he said, suddenly aware again of his own pangs of helplessness and hopelessness. "What happened to them, anyway?"

"Adversity of all different kinds," Doc explained. "Some have experienced unfortunate events. They have lost something—a love, a job, a home—maybe everything. Some have been mistreated. Some are lonely. Some are ill. Some have been unhappy for a long time with one aspect or another of their lives or the people in their lives. They have too much of this or too little of that. They do not want what they have and they want what they do not have."

"That's so true," added Maxine. "It seems like half of them want a partner and the other half have one they don't want."

Doc agreed. "Yes, and many are angry with themselves for mistakes they have made or with people who have 'done them wrong,' perhaps as long as twenty, thirty, forty years ago or longer. Every kind of problem you can think of is represented here."

"So they just hang around feeling sorry for themselves and carrying on about their troubles?"

"Some do," Doc answered. "They hardly eat, work, or have the energy to do much of anything. However, many are extremely busy, mostly doing things to help themselves forget."

"Like what? Besides spinning their wheels."

"Like bingeing on food, juice, or work, or going on shopping sprees at the Bleaksville Mall."

Duke sighed. "Some things are so bad they could make anyone feel miserable enough to do desperate things."

Maxine flew onto his shoulder and tapped him with her foot, reminding him to think about his thinking. He quickly corrected himself. "Of course the things themselves couldn't make them feel or do anything. A + B = C. They must have learned that on the Path of Serenity like I did."

"Some did," Doc said. "However, when it became too difficult, they gave up, at least for a time. Many travelers on the Path of Serenity take one step backward for every two steps forward. This is one of their steps back. It can happen to anyone. If they stay, though, that is another matter entirely."

"And," Maxine continued, "there are people here who don't know anything about the path or the ABCs. Isn't that right, Doc? They came by alternate routes, convinced they ended up in Bleaksville because life did them in."

"Yes," Doc said, "and they too may stay for years—even their entire lifetimes."

Duke cupped his hands over his ears. "All this wailing and moaning and yelling and whining sure can get on a person's nerves. How do they stand it?"

Doc replied, "Those who stay get so used to it that it seems normal. So does spending such inordinate amounts of time thinking about what is wrong in their lives that they can hardly remember what is right. They get absorbed in their own small, small world, shutting out thoughts of those people outside Bleaksville who have problems as bad or worse than theirs but don't make self-pity their life's work."

"You mean like George, the dragon slayer–turned–sports announcer?" Duke said, uncomfortably aware of how unlike George he was at the moment.

Maxine answered, "Yes, he's a real straight thinker. He had better things to do than to stay around here, making himself angrier and more depressed than he already was. He wasn't about to turn his Type I heavy heart into a Type II."

"People think they are *living* here," Doc said. "Actually they are *dying* here, a little more each day. They don't even notice the sunsets or hear the birds sing."

"Why don't they just leave?" Duke asked, knowing he was on the brink of becoming one of them.

"They say their hearts are too heavy to climb over the fence," Doc said.

Duke looked at the fence. "It's just a low picket fence. It wouldn't take much to get over it. And what about the gate? They could probably open it and walk right out."

"The way out may seem obvious to you. However, people on the inside have a different perspective. They cannot always see what those of us on the outside can see. For many, Bleaksville becomes their home. They do not like it much but they are used to it. That makes it comfortable, in an uncomfortable sort of way."

"Can't you tell them how to get out?"

"We do," said Maxine. "We tell them the way out is the same as the way not to get in in the first place: Accept the things you can't change and change the things you can. Some don't listen. You can't force people to do what they don't want to do."

"Unfortunately," Doc went on, "residents keep agonizing over the things they cannot change, and they neglect to change the things they can—even though they are miserable. Sometimes the situation is even worse. They accept things they need to change and try to change things they need to accept, substantially compounding their adversities. They don't have the wisdom to tell the difference."

"The way I feel now, I could easily join them," Duke said sadly, the sound of their agony rumbling in his ears.

All at once the gate swung open invitingly.

Duke fell to his knees. "I don't want to live here! I don't want to be their neighbor!" He looked up pleadingly at Doc and Maxine. "What will it take for me to get away from here?"

"Some straight thinking and some courage," Doc said.

"Courage to do what?"

"What do *you* think?" the owl asked.

At that moment Duke remembered the sign at the entrance to the Land of Courage. "To change the things I can?"

"That's it!" Maxine said. "The law of the land."

Duke was frustrated. "Don't you think I would change everything if I could? I'm a disgrace! I've lost my title. I'm probably being brought up on disciplinary charges. I can't change any of that! And I can't accept it either." He hung his head in shame. "It's all over for me."

"It's never over till it's over," Maxine replied in a cheerful voice that Duke found annoying.

"Said like a true bluebird of happiness," he grumbled, looking up at her. "It's all so horrific, so ghastly, so wretched."

Maxine cringed and covered her face with her wing.

"Don't look at me like that, please, Max," Duke pleaded. "I didn't say what happened was awful or terrible."

"You might as well have. You're still saying the same kind of thing *they* would say," she snapped, pointing with her wing. "You know, you don't have to be here anymore than they do — no matter what's happened, no matter what's wrong."

"That is true," Doc agreed. "They give in to their crooked thinking. The question now is, are you going to become Bleaksville's newest resident by giving in to *your* crooked thinking? Or are you going to straighten it out, accept what you need to, change what you need to, and get on with your journey?"

"Come on, Duke. You don't want me to be reassigned, do you?" Maxine coaxed.

Thoughts raced through Duke's mind. His heart suddenly started to pound, as if it were demanding its wishes be heard. He looked through the open gate at the misery that would be his future if he couldn't get himself away from Bleaksville.

He stared at the satchel on the ground next to him. Deep in thought, he opened it and reached inside. He put on his New View glasses and took a swig of O Well water, and then another. He clutched the stone and stick in one hand and opened his book of lessons for the heart with the other.

After a while he put his hero tools back into the satchel, struggled to his feet, and slung the bag over his shoulder.

"There's no way I'm staying here in ... in Whine Whine Park to spin my wheels and binge with them," he announced.

Doc and Maxine nodded in approval.

Duke took a deep breath. "What happened, happened, and somehow I'll find a way to survive even though it doesn't feel like it yet. I don't know what I can possibly change, but I'm ready to get back on the Path of Serenity and find out."

Maxine hopped up and down with excitement. "Good work, Duke!" she chirped. "You had the courage to start changing something already—your view! Now I'd like to change *my* view. Let's get out of here."

CHAPTER FIFTEEN

An Ordinary Hero

Before the tired, heavy-hearted dragon slayer and his feathered guides could reach the Path of Serenity, Doc received an emergency call. The owl reassured Duke that he was making good progress and that Maxine was particularly knowledgeable in the courage and changing things department. Then he flew away.

"Duke, Duke!" Maxine called from above. "We're almost back to the path. I see it just ahead."

"That's good, but please tell me you haven't spotted any more detours," Duke said wearily. Wanting serenity more than ever, he picked up the pace. Although walking fast was particularly tiring for a man with a heavy heart and satchel, he kept pushing himself.

As soon as they got to the path, another sign greeted them:

BRIDGE OF CHANGE STRAIGHT AHEAD

"Bridge of Change? What's that?" Duke asked, collapsing onto a wooden bench near the sign.

Maxine landed beside him. "It's a bridge that connects what *is* with what will *be*."

"I wish I didn't have to think about what will be. I dread going home. Even my lessons and hero tools haven't been enough to change that. What am I going to do, Max?"

"To start with, you're going to change your belief that you're nothing without your title and the respect of your fellow heroes and the adoration of cheering crowds," the bluebird responded, tapping his leg with her wing for emphasis.

A look of dejection crossed Duke's face. In a quavering voice he said, "But it's true."

"Where's the proof?" asked Maxine.

"Oh yeah, the disputing. Well, I . . . um, I guess technically there isn't any proof, but—"

"No buts about it," Maxine interrupted, fluffing her feathers. "You're thinking crooked again, measuring your whole self by how well you do things. You need to think logically about this, Duke. You do lots of things—some good, some not so good. And you may do the same thing well at one time and not another. So how can you possibly base your opinion of yourself—your entire worth as a person—on any one or even some of the things you do?"

"Hmm. I never thought of it that way. But isn't it natural to feel good when you succeed and bad when you don't?"

"Of course, but that doesn't mean you're a good or bad person because of it."

"Even though I've really messed up?"

"Yes. You *are not* what you *do*. Look, you've had some problems and made some mistakes. That only proves you've had some problems and made some mistakes. It doesn't prove you have less worth than you did before. And being a famous dragon slayer didn't make you have *more* worth either. Your value as a human being hasn't changed. Basically, that's it."

"That's it?"

"Yes, everyone has problems at times and everyone—even

the most successful people—makes mistakes. People are fallible. Big deal. That's the way nature made them. So what? Duke, you're still taking things too seriously. I think you could use some more O Well water," she said playfully.

"It's not like I just have some problems and made some mistakes." He looked away and took a deep breath. "I've failed—at everything."

Maxine looked at him quizzically. "Is that really true?"

"Well, there's no proof. I guess I'm exaggerating."

"That's a good start. Now how is thinking that way making you feel?"

"Pretty bad. But even if I don't exaggerate, I still failed at a bunch of stuff."

"Failures aren't failures the way you think they are, Duke. They're teachers in disguise—teachers that guide you toward success."

Duke rolled his eyes. "Oh yeah, my failures are guiding me right up the ladder of success. I'm getting up so high I may get a nosebleed."

Maxine smiled. "Perception is everything. I know you don't believe this now, but one day you'll look back and realize that your problems, mistakes, and failures have been your greatest teachers."

"Now you're saying that my problems and mistakes are teachers too?" he said, his brow furrowed.

"Well, they got you onto the Path of Serenity, which is probably the best thing that could've happened to you. Just wait until you see what good things come from your having been in a bad spot."

As Duke thought about all he had learned since starting out on the path, he knew that Maxine was right, as usual. And he realized his tiny companion was one of the good things that had already come out of his being in a bad spot.

"Okay, so if I dispute my crooked thoughts, I might be able to change the way I feel about myself," he said finally. "But what about the way everyone else feels about me? They're going to judge me by what happened. And I can't change that."

"Some may judge you," Maxine replied gently. "Do you really think, though, that all the people who have loved you and counted on you over the years will think less of you because you had a rough time for a while? You're being harder on yourself than most of them will be."

"Maybe. Maybe not."

"Oh Duke, you're giving other people entirely too much power over you. You may feel bad if some of them think less of you but you can't base your feelings about yourself on what anyone else *thinks* any more than you can base it on what you *do*."

"Then what *can* I base them on?" Duke asked, still frustrated.

"On a decision to consider yourself a worthwhile person, no matter what, just because you exist. The end." Maxine spread her wings and cocked her head. "It's that simple."

Duke was distressed. "You mean that everyone's worth is the same and no one has to earn it? That doesn't sound right. Doesn't that make everyone, well ... ordinary?"

"People can *be* ordinary human beings and still *do* extraordinary things. In fact, many ordinary people living ordinary lives act heroically. If the world finds out about their heroism, they may be labeled heroes and become famous, but they're still ordinary people who acted heroically. And so are people like you who make a profession of being heroic."

Duke looked doubtful. "But everyone called me a hero. I was famous."

"Fame doesn't define heroism. Courage does. You were called a hero because you often acted courageously. You felt fear and did what was necessary anyway. And that's exactly what you're doing on this path."

"Does that mean I'm still sort of a hero?"

"You are what you were before—a worthwhile person who often acts courageously."

Duke thought and thought, trying to figure out if what he had always believed about himself and others was true. Then he thought hard about the thoughts he had had about himself since his life had run amok—thoughts that had made him feel worthless. He asked himself all the right questions about truth and results, challenging and reasoning and trying to change his crooked thoughts.

Maxine said softly, "There's something in your satchel that can help you stop measuring things that aren't meant to be measured."

Duke reached into his bag. He found the measuring tape and looked it over. "Hey, this thing has no numbers on it! It doesn't even have those little lines!"

"Exactly," Maxine said.

Duke stared at the blank tape, fully aware that a momentous decision awaited him—one that he knew would send ripples throughout his entire life.

A realization dawned upon him. "I've been measuring myself ever since I can remember, trying to prove that I'm okay, that I'm good, that I'm the best. But I'll never do it again. I'm changing the way I think of myself and other people. No more measuring my whole self," he said decisively, tossing the tape back into his satchel.

"Does that mean you no longer consider yourself a worthless, pathetic, stupid old has-been?"

"That's what it means, all right," he answered, smiling the smile of a man who had just had a heavy burden lifted off his shoulders—although in Duke's case, it was his heart. It definitely felt lighter again. He was so elated he could hardly concentrate as he wrote his latest lessons in his book.

LESSONS ABOUT BEING GOOD ENOUGH

1. *No more measuring myself or others.*
2. *I am a valuable person just because I exist.*
3. *I am okay because of who I am, not what I do.*
4. *Everyone makes mistakes.*
5. *Problems, mistakes, and failures are teachers.*
6. *Most people won't be as hard on me as I am on myself.*

CHAPTER SIXTEEN

The Leap of Faith

When Duke finished writing in his book, he and Maxine set off again on the path as it wound toward the Bridge of Change. Feeling hopeful and eager to get on with his journey, Duke pondered the Law of the Land of Courage: Change the things you can.

He thought back over all the things he had already changed, things he had once thought he couldn't. And he wondered if maybe he could also change some of the other things he had thought he couldn't. Not wanting to confuse what can be changed with what needs to be accepted—as did many Bleaksvillites, perish the thought—he asked Maxine how to tell one from the other.

"You've been learning that all along," she said, flying in a zigzag pattern just ahead.

"I've been learning a lot, but I'm still not sure if I could really change things if I go home. When I first heard how much trouble I was in with the Dragon Slayers Association I was positive I couldn't change anything, but now…" His voice trailed off.

"That was your emotions talking—emotions that came from crooked thinking," explained Maxine. "You're thinking straighter now. Reason and logic are kicking in. That's the key."

"Will it ever get easier to know what to accept and what to change?"

"Yes, your wisdom to know the difference will keep growing as long as you keep thinking straight and paying attention to what works and what doesn't."

"Hmm. Is there anything that'll help me tell the difference in the meantime?"

"You might try asking yourself what you would advise someone else to do in the same situation. That will get your emotions out of the way and help you use reason instead of wishful thinking or fearful thinking."

"What if I don't know what to tell anyone else either?" Duke asked, perplexed.

Maxine landed on his shoulder. "Look, Duke. It's not as hard as it sounds. Things you have control over you may be able to change. Things you don't have control over you need to accept. Knowing one from the other is simply a matter of common sense and experience."

"What about situations I have only *some* control over, like those that involve other people?"

"In that case, you do as much as you can to change your part in the situation. That's all you can do. The rest is up to the others." Maxine began preening her feathers.

Duke started asking about the association's disciplinary committee and the other things he had in mind to change. Like any good guide, Maxine answered his questions with questions that helped him find his own answers.

But the more he thought about what he might be able to change, and the more he weighed their pros and cons, the more afraid he became—afraid of not knowing what *would* happen and afraid of what he thought *might* happen.

Changing things was not child's play. It was scary business. Very scary business. And he became plenty scared just thinking about it.

As he walked along, lost in his thoughts, a light fog appeared. It became thicker as they continued on.

All of a sudden the path ahead stopped at a steep cliff. Almost everything beyond it was engulfed in moist whiteness. Duke could hear the roar of a raging river below. Cautiously he inched up to the edge to get a better look.

"Whoa! What is this place?" he asked.

"It's the Leap of Faith," Maxine said, pointing her wing at a sign posted on a nearby tree.

Duke looked at the sign. "I didn't see that," he said, rather flustered. "I guess I'm in a fog in more ways than one. Hey, what happened to the path? It's gone."

"No it isn't. The Leap of Faith is part of the path, like the schoolhouse was, remember? In fact, the leap leads to the Bridge of Change."

"You mean it's out there somewhere?" he asked, squinting into the whiteness. "If only this darn fog wasn't so thick."

"The Fog of Uncertainty obscures your view when you fear the unknown," Maxine explained.

"No wonder I can't see," Duke said. "Oh look, way out there. I think I can make out part of the bridge. Is it made of rope, with heavy rope sides and all?"

Maxine nodded. "Yes, that's it. When you're ready you can leap right onto it and be home in no time."

"Leap? Are you kidding?" Duke was incredulous. "There's no way I could leap across there, not and survive! The bridge is too far away."

"Fear makes the leap look bigger than it is," Maxine said. "You need to replace your fears with faith."

"Faith in what?"

"In yourself and your ability to get through whatever comes up when you change things."

"Oh, is that all?" Duke said flippantly.

"No," replied Maxine seriously, "you also need to have faith that the universe will support you if you let go and trust it to take care of what you can't take care of."

"I don't know," Duke said, looking down into the rushing water. I sure don't want to end up down there. I could drown."

"Lots of people who don't have faith in themselves or the universe say that. They're afraid to take a leap of faith. But if they've learned how to swim, chances are good they'll survive even if they fall into troubled waters. And the universe has an impressive fleet of lifeboats that somehow seem to show up when least expected—often when all else fails."

"Very funny, Max."

"I wasn't trying to be funny."

Duke swallowed hard. "Lifeboats or no lifeboats, I'm afraid of ending up in troubled waters if I try to change things. I mean I could go back and talk to the disciplinary committee, but that might make things even worse. And if they don't throw me out of the association altogether I could try to get my title back, but what if I can't do it? I could try to change my relationship with Jonathan, but he was so angry with me he might never want to see me again. I could change my mind about never trusting or getting involved with another woman, but what if someone else dumps me like Allie and Cindy did? I'm so afraid just thinking about what could happen if I try to change things that I'll never be able to. I mean, everything could go wrong and I'd be sorry I ever tried and—"

"STOP!" Maxine shouted, putting up her wing to halt the onslaught of crooked thinking. "You're scaring yourself about things that may never happen!"

"But they *could*, right?"

"Maybe. If so you'll deal with them. Have you forgotten your ABCs? If some things don't work out the way you want them to, it'll be too bad but not awful or terrible. You'll survive. You're exaggerating valid concerns into paralyzing fears."

"Exaggerating? Does that mean I have to—you know, the D word?"

Maxine nodded.

Duke groaned and wandered over to a boulder a few feet away. He sat down and placed his satchel beside him. One by one he disputed the thoughts that were creating his fears. He muttered and he yelled and he read from his book of lessons for the heart. Every so often he grabbed one or another of his hero tools, and when each had done its job of helping him to see more clearly or feel calmer or remember an important lesson, he dropped it back into the satchel.

Battle weary, he finally closed the book and set it down. He gazed out over the cliff. Things had changed—in more ways than one.

"Look, Max, you were right. I think there's a little less fog and the bridge is a little closer than I thought." Then he paused. "But it's still much too far away to leap onto. I guess my feelings didn't straighten out as much as my thoughts," he said, disappointed.

"You're doing fine, Duke," Maxine assured him. "You know that changing your feelings can take time. There's a way to hurry it up, though. You could start *acting* against your fears as well as *thinking* against them. That's part of the secret, remember? Acting against your crooked thoughts."

"*Acting* against them?"

"Yes, doing what you're afraid of."

Duke shook his head slowly. "I knew you were going to say that. But how can I do what I'm afraid of? I'm still too afraid."

"You could practice being less afraid," Maxine said brightly.

"Doc has an amazing trick that works for all kinds of bad feelings. It will whittle down those fears before you know it."

Although considerably less enthusiastic than Maxine, Duke was encouraged by a renegade vision of himself whittling down his fears like Willie whittled wood. "Okay. What's the trick?"

Under Maxine's direction, Duke closed his eyes and imagined himself appearing before the disapproving, stone-faced members of the disciplinary committee and letting himself feel the fear he felt every time he thought about facing them.

"Now make your fear stronger," she instructed, "as strong as you possibly can."

He let his crooked thinking run wild. His heart pounded and he shook inside. His throat went dry and his palms grew moist. "Okay," he choked, "I did it."

"Now you've created your feelings, and you can change them. Keep imagining staring into those same faces and reduce your fear with some straight thinking."

A flurry of straight thoughts pushed out the crooked ones, and Duke's paralyzing fear released him from its grip. "Whoa! That felt so real! I can't believe I got my fear to let up like that, right in the middle of one of my worst nightmares. But I did, and here I am. I survived. How about that!"

Maxine was delighted. "You're in training for conquering your fears like you were once in training for conquering dragons. You'll feel stronger and braver when the real thing comes. Isn't it wonderful!"

Duke didn't know if wonderful was the right word, but if his training for fears worked half as well as his training for dragons, maybe he could go back and face the committee after all. On second thought, maybe wonderful was the right word.

Hopeful, he looked into the fog. It had lifted a little more and the bridge seemed slightly closer, but not close enough.

He decided that if he was ever going to take that leap and get on his way, he had better work on the rest of his fears. Although Maxine cautioned him about doing too many at once, he had tasted success and would not be dissuaded.

After whittling down some of his other fears, he looked into the fog again. It had thinned out a little more and the bridge looked even closer, but leaping onto it still seemed impossible.

"It's natural to have some fear when facing a risk, Duke. You're tired. It's been a long day. Why don't we talk about it in the morning?"

Max always knows what I need, he thought.

They ate what food they could gather and made a bed for Duke from some loose foliage. After Maxine flew off to find herself a comfortable place to sleep, Duke glanced around and listened intently for any sign of the Dragon of Crooked Thinking. Satisfied that he was safe for the time being, he took a sip of O Well water to relax his mind and looked up into the endless, dark blue sky.

"Please," he implored, "help me get the wisdom to know what I can change—and the courage to change it."

He pulled his satchel of hero tools close, nestled into the protection of the soft leaves, and slipped into a deep sleep, murmuring "Please...please...please."

That night he had a disturbing dream. In the dream he felt himself leaping off the cliff and falling down, down into the treacherous water and being swallowed up, never to be heard from again.

Duke awoke and sat bolt upright, shaken. Upset and alone in the dark of night, he couldn't think straight, but he didn't want to wake Maxine. Besides, he was becoming better at straightening out his thinking. He calmed himself in short order and fell back to sleep.

When Duke awoke in the morning and told Maxine about his dream, doubts crept in. "I might not end up any better off than I am now." "I mean, I could be just trading one set of problems for another. Or things might get even worse. How do I know trying to change things will be worth it?"

Accustomed to dealing with such doubts, Maxine replied, "That excuse keeps many people from doing what they need to do to be happier. What's the alternative? To sit around wishing things were different? To hope that some way, somehow, something will change—and then putting up with or settling for whatever drifts your way? If you don't decide, life will decide for you—and you'll still be responsible for the outcome."

Duke raised his eyebrows. "You mean if I don't try to change the things I can, whatever happens is still my fault?"

"Your responsibility," she corrected. "Not making a decision is a decision. It affects what happens. If you do nothing, you'll usually get nothing, except more of the same—or worse. Could you live with that? Would you be getting what you want, what is important to you, what you deserve? Would you be happy?"

Duke shook his head. "No, settling isn't my style. I'm a take-charge kind of guy. My hero ways, you know. Even so…"

"You want a guarantee. I wish I could give you one. I can't. No one can. Taking risks is part of making changes, part of doing anything new, part of living. You know that. You've taken risks all your life—some of them big ones. And if you hadn't, you wouldn't have achieved all you did."

"I guess not," he said glumly.

"Think back, Duke. Didn't you risk failing or getting hurt every time you took a training class, every time you went off to fight a dragon?"

"Uh-huh, I was scared lots of times."

"What did you do?"

"Well, I must have talked myself out of it, probably using some heavy-duty straight thinking like I did with Doc's trick. Back then I didn't know I was doing it, that's all."

"What else did you do to overcome your fear?"

"I'm not sure. I was expected to be courageous, and I wanted so much to become the number one dragon slayer that I just made myself do whatever I had to to make it happen."

"So you forced yourself to take action, to do what was best for you, in spite of your fears?"

"Yeah. And it seemed to get easier as I went along."

"Courage is like that. The more courageous you are, the more courageous you become."

"Hmm, that's interesting. It takes courage to have courage."

"Yes, much like you have to slay dragons to become a dragon slayer," Maxine said.

Duke wondered why such obvious truths hadn't occurred to him before.

Maxine continued, "Can you think of anything else that made it easier to do what you feared—something that might help you now?"

"Let's see . . ."

"What about your dragon-slaying strategies?"

"You mean like my famous weather trick and expert moves? It's true, slaying dragons wasn't nearly as scary when I knew I had a good plan worked out ahead of time. And it did put me at a definite tactical advantage."

Duke thought for a moment. Suddenly he blurted out, "Hey, I could plan what to say and do at the disciplinary committee meeting. Yeah! Get a good strategy going. That could work for getting my title back too, and all the other stuff I need to change!"

"Good idea, Duke," Maxine said. "It's easier to have faith that you can handle whatever happens when you're well prepared. Be flexible, though," she cautioned. "You know what they say about the best-laid plans of mice and men—and even bluebirds."

Duke grimaced as he thought back over plans he had had that went awry because of unexpected turns of events. But he hadn't known about being flexible then. He had thought everything had to happen the way he thought it should. And when it didn't he had fought it instead of adjusting his plan. Now he knew better.

He picked up his book of lessons for the heart, and while Maxine flitted around enjoying the scenery, he wrote all he had learned since making his last entry. Then he thought and planned and strategized, and even came up with contingency plans in case something unexpected happened.

As he focused on how he was going to bring about the changes he wanted, visions of talking the committee out of taking disciplinary action, of regaining his title, and of having a loving relationship with Jonathan and getting on better terms with Allie paraded before Duke's eyes. Just *planning* to take action made him feel better.

Then, quite unexpectedly, his thoughts shifted to bittersweet memories of his life with Allie. "It's too bad that what happened, happened," he said. "Allie and I both made mistakes—mistakes I'll never make again. I guess mistakes really are teachers."

"That's the kind of straight thinking that can open up interesting new options," Maxine remarked, hovering next to him.

Duke raised his eyebrows. "Do you think so? Like what?"

She landed on his satchel. "You never know what might happen. Accepting the unacceptable sometimes makes it possible to change it."

An old familiar feeling deep inside him began to stir. "What's going on, Max?" he asked. "I feel kind of funny."

Maxine started jumping up and down. "You whittled down your fears enough to change your view of change! Duke, this is great! You're getting back what you lost!"

"What? What did I lose? he asked. "Besides my title, I mean, and my reputation and my wife and—"

"Why, your sense of adventure!" Maxine chirped, waving her wings. "Your thrill of the contest! Your excitement for challenge! That's what!"

"You don't mean I'm getting excited about appearing before the disciplinary committee and struggling to get my title back and all that?" he asked skeptically.

"Yes, yes you are! Why wouldn't you? You know you have a good chance of changing things. You can make a difference and you know it. Don't you see? Instead of scaring yourself with the *worst* that could happen, you're exciting yourself with the *best* that could happen! Fear begets fear, and courage begets courage!"

"I do feel excitement sort of taking over the fear. No, it's more like the fear is charged with excitement, like it used to be when I was learning how to slay dragons. Come to think of it, I did used to get excited about the best that could happen. Why, I remember dreaming—"

Duke stopped abruptly. It had been a long time since he had risked telling anything private to a female. With Maxine, though, it was different. He felt safe with her. In all their time together she had never judged him, never criticized him, never become angry with him—unlike some people he knew. He had doubts about lots of things these days and he couldn't count on much of anything. But he had no doubts about Maxine, and she was always there when he needed her.

He looked into her accepting little eyes and knew he could

tell her anything. "I remember dreaming of becoming a famous dragon slayer. I even pretended I already was one. I saw myself all grown up, racing through town in a bright red dragon wagon past cheering crowds, and I saw my portrait on the Wall of Fame at the Hero Shoppe next to my father's and grandfather's."

Maxine tilted her head, listening intently.

"Then when I was a rising star in the dragon-slaying business, I would imagine myself an invincible superhero, as fast as a bolt of lightning, as powerful as a tornado, and able to slay my prey with a single thrust of my sword. Sometimes I would even pose in front of a mirror.

"Well, anyway," he mumbled, suddenly embarrassed by his gush of sentimentality, "so much for our trip down memory lane. I forgot why I even started telling you all this."

"Maybe because you're recognizing that hopes and dreams and seeing yourself as you would like to be can all help build the courage to go after what you want. They can also set the wheels of the universe in motion to help you."

"I'm not so sure about that universe stuff, but I have enough faith in myself now to change what needs to be changed and to live through whatever happens. Hopefully that'll be enough."

"Maybe, but what about the times you asked the universe for help?"

"I asked just in case there was anyone or anything out there. I was desperate. I didn't know what else to do. I had tried everything I could, and it wasn't enough. My whole life had run amok and I didn't know how to set it right."

Maxine raised her wing. "My point exactly. When you've done all you can and it isn't enough, turning the situation over to something more powerful than yourself can make all the difference. When you crashed your dragon wagon and thought all was lost, you asked for help and the universe sent Doc."

"Yeah, but that could have been a coincidence."

"What about when you asked for help accepting the things you couldn't change?"

"Maybe that wasn't because of the universe either. It could have been because I worked so hard on my lessons."

"Could be, but where did the lessons come from, and the teachers and new hero tools, precisely when you needed them? The universe works quietly behind the scenes. It can help you best when you're aware of it and accepting of its gifts—when you do all you can, and then let go and get out of its way and trust that it will take care of the rest."

Duke sighed. "You mean when I can't do any more, just turn it over to the universe? It would be a relief to do that. But how can I get that kind of faith when I have doubts?"

"The same way you get courage—by having it. You decide to have it and act as if you have it."

Duke sighed again. "Okay, I'll try."

"A decision to try gives you an out. It's not a firm commitment."

"All right. I'll do it," he said, this time with conviction. "I have faith. I decided."

"Good!" exclaimed Maxine. "That's the spirit. Now are you ready to *act* as if you have it and take that leap?"

He looked out toward the bridge. For the first time, it looked close enough to leap onto—then again, maybe not. It would be a risky leap at best, especially since it was still foggy.

His heart thumped in his chest. "Can't we do something to clear up the fog first?"

"Getting through the Fog of Uncertainty is part of change. You've already cleared some of it by fighting your fears. The fog won't completely clear until you're past it."

Duke took a deep breath. "Ask me again, Max. Ask me if I'm ready."

"Are you ready to take the leap? What do you say?"

Duke took another deep breath. "I say . . . okay. After all, as you said, what's the alternative?"

At that very moment the hairs on the back of his neck stood on end, and his thumping heart kicked into high gear. The air vibrated with anticipation, and a familiar pounding shook the ground, except now something was unmistakably different about it.

Duke sprang to his feet, ready to face what was coming. His first thought was to reach for his sword, but this time he remembered and grabbed his satchel of new hero tools instead.

"Okay, where are you?" he bellowed. "Let's get this over with. I have no time to waste."

CHAPTER SEVENTEEN

The Moment of Surrender

Standing tall, Duke turned in the direction of the pounding sound. He saw a small dragon coming toward him, stomping the ground with as much force as his weak little legs could muster. It was a pathetic sight.

The dragon slayer was stunned. "Is that you?" he asked, craning his neck. "The granddaddy of all dragons? Look, Max! Can you believe it!"

"No need to rub it in," the dragon hissed, struggling to make his croaky, weak voice sound as strong as he possibly could.

"Why are you stomping your feet like that?" the dragon slayer asked.

"I'm used to making an entrance."

"You made one all right. You're so small!"

"Don't judge me by my size," the dragon sneered. "I'm still powerful."

"So am I," Duke countered emphatically. "I've worked hard to straighten out my thinking and build my courage to change the things I can."

"You got it, pal. You've been killing me with all the talk and fear-whittling tricks and hero tools!"

"That's the idea," Duke shot back. "And don't call me pal. You're no pal of mine."

"Aren't we touchy today," the dragon said sarcastically. "Well, pal or no pal, I know how to get to you. Dragons have battle plans too, you know. And I hope this time you won't take unfair advantage by using the stuff in that bag. Whatever happened to winning your battles fair and square?"

"Get to the point, will you? I've got a leap to take."

"That's what I came to talk to you about. If you're fool enough to take that leap, you're going to end up smashed to pieces over those rocks down there in that raging water! Is that what you want?"

"If that's what you came here to tell me, you wasted a trip. We've argued this to death already—pardon the pun. I'm taking the leap and that's final. Do I need to remind you what happened the last time you showed up and we had a war of words? You got so small and weak it took you three tries to disappear."

"It's different this time. You can't prove me wrong."

"About what? Oh, never mind. It doesn't matter. I've made my decision. It's the logical thing to do." Duke hugged the satchel to his chest. "Whatever happens, I have faith in myself to handle it and faith in the universe to take care of what I can't. I can hardly wait to get back and start making some changes."

"You've made a decision. Big deal. People make decisions all the time—and we talk them out of following through all the time."

Duke didn't expect to hear this. "Who's we? You mean there are more of you?"

"Sure. Everyone has a dragon of crooked thinking. Now let's see, where was I before you changed the subject? Ah, yes—decisions. No problem. A commitment—now that's harder to stop. Even so, if you were committed to taking that leap—which you're not—I could still scare you out of it."

"How? By throwing a few sparks at me?"

"Nah, I'm not into that stuff anymore. That showy stuff is for ordinary dragons."

"Fine, whatever. I refuse to discuss my decision or my commitment with you. I'm ready to go."

"Fine, whatever," mimicked the dragon.

"Aren't you going to try to stop me?"

"If you have the courage, go ahead," the dragon said, nodding toward the cliff.

That couldn't be all there was to it. Duke's stomach started to churn, which was never a good sign. "Are you going to stand there and watch?"

The dragon sat back on his hind legs. "Yeah, thanks for the invitation. This should be quite entertaining."

There was nothing else to do but leap. Duke looked over at Maxine. "Will you come with me?" he asked with concern. She nodded.

Duke set down his satchel next to her, walked up to the cliff, and examined the ground along the edge. When he found a suitable flat spot that would give him a solid footing, he marked it by setting a large rock beside it. Then he retrieved his satchel, slipped it on, and tightened the strap, securing it over his shoulder. He walked back far enough to take a long, running leap. Maxine followed him.

Poised like a racehorse at the starting gate, he waited for the right moment. Maxine stood in readiness beside him. He looked at the dragon, then back at the spot he had marked.

"This is it," he said resolutely. "Here I go." And he was off and running, with Maxine hopping along beside him.

"WAIT!" the dragon suddenly called out.

Duke skidded to a stop. So did Maxine.

"Uh, excuse me," the dragon said, waving his front claws. "Are you at all concerned about leaping across with that satchel? It could knock you off balance."

"What about that, Max?" Duke whispered.

She whispered back, "People leap all the time carrying all kinds of baggage. You can make it."

Duke turned to the dragon. "People do it all the time carrying all kinds of baggage. I can make it."

The dragon shrugged his sloping shoulders. "Just trying to be helpful." It was a funny sight but Duke was in no mood to enjoy it.

He and Maxine backed up and started again. They got as far as they had the last time when again the dragon shouted "WAIT!"

Again they stopped. "*Now* what?" Duke asked impatiently.

"Uh, excuse me, just one more thing," the dragon said. "What about the extra weight of your heavy heart? You know what happened when you leaped off the cliff on your last dragon-slaying mission. Just thought I'd mention it."

"What about that, Max?" Duke whispered nervously, remembering what a disaster that mission had been. "My heart's not as heavy as it was then, but it isn't exactly light yet."

She whispered back, "It's no problem, Duke. Most people taking this leap—"

"Why are we whispering?" Duke interrupted. "Why don't you tell the dragon yourself so I don't have to repeat it to him?"

"Because he's *your* dragon," she stated quietly. "Tell him that most people taking this leap have heavy hearts—that you can make it."

"Okay," Duke replied. "Hey, dragon," he yelled. "No problem. Most people taking this leap have heavy hearts. I can make it."

"Just trying to be helpful," the dragon said, shrugging again.

"I don't want to let him keep stopping me, Max, but I get really nervous that he might bring up something important I didn't think of."

"He's trying to give you the last-minute jitters. It's part of his strategy. But it won't work if you focus on your faith and do what you need to do."

Duke told the dragon not to bother stopping him this time because it wouldn't work. He had come too far to let last-minute jitters unnerve him before his big leap.

He and Maxine backed up and started again.

"WAIT!" the dragon called out. Duke ignored him and kept running toward the cliff, picking up speed. Just before he got to the edge the dragon thundered, "HOW DO YOU KNOW IT'S TRUE THE UNIVERSE WILL BE THERE FOR YOU? WHERE'S THE PROOF?"

Duke stopped so abruptly that he nearly toppled over and fell off the cliff. Shaken, he dropped to the ground.

"Proof?" he said, dismayed. "I didn't think to ask for proof, Max. How do I know the universe being there for me isn't only a bunch of mumbo jumbo? The dragon could be right. It could be nothing but a big pile of crooked thinking!"

"Ha! I *knew* it!" the dragon gloated. "This time I made you provide the proof! You may have faith in *yourself* but you don't have faith in the *universe*. No proof, no faith, no courage, no leap! Ha!" As he said this, his voice grew stronger and his body larger.

Duke looked at Maxine with pleading eyes.

She hopped closer to him and said, "Apples fall from trees. They don't float off into the air. You can't see what makes them fall but it's there just the same. You can't see a gentle breeze but you can feel it. Some things are like that. It's their nature to *be* without being seen. Once they have been felt, really felt, no ordinary proof is necessary."

Duke perked up. "You mean with some things signs are enough proof?"

"Yes, and in time you will have all the proof you need for lasting faith. In the meantime, fake it until you make it. You know how to do that."

Duke stared out over the cliff, thinking about everything Maxine had said. A question came into his mind. "If the universe takes care of what I can't, why doesn't it make this an easy leap? I've done my part."

"Maybe it will," was all Maxine could say.

"Don't bet on it," sniped the dragon, who was moving closer and straining to hear what they were saying.

Keeping his voice low so as not to encourage any more of the dragon's snide remarks, Duke said, "I was ready to take the leap, Max. I was right at the edge. You saw me. And the universe didn't do anything to help me."

"The universe works on its own schedule, not yours," she replied. "You need to trust that it knows *what* is right and *when* it's right, better than you do. Besides, you're asking the Leap of Faith to change its nature."

Duke looked puzzled.

"It wouldn't be the Leap of Faith if it took no faith to leap," she explained.

"I get it. Stones are hard and stars shine. I don't know...I want to believe in the power of the universe but somehow I need more help with this, Max."

"I'm not the one you need to ask."

"Who is, Doc?"

"No. What you need is a different kind of help than a friend or teacher, even a wise one, can give. Whom did you ask for help before when there was no one else?"

Duke knew immediately what Maxine meant. He glanced over at the dragon. "In front of *him*?" he asked, jabbing a thumb in the beast's direction. "I don't know. I've always done this alone."

"When you talk to the universe, it's a private moment no matter who is there."

Knowing it was true, Duke closed his eyes and lowered his head. "Please, please," he whispered, "help me find the faith I need to take this leap."

Then he waited silently.

This time the answer came swiftly. A new voice bubbled up inside him: "The proof you want is in the doing."

"What?" Duke said, startled.

"The proof you want is in the doing," the voice repeated.

Duke jumped to his feet. "Come on, Maxine. Let's do it!"

The bluebird leaped into the air. "Why, that's the first time you've called me Maxine! You're starting to trust again!"

"I figure it's one leap of faith I can take without risking a free fall into oblivion." He grinned, pulled his satchel over his shoulder, checked to make sure the strap was tight, and strode back to the spot he had started out from three times before.

Immediately the dragon began getting smaller. Agitated, he tried to shout, but his voice was smaller too. "You're a fool! This is suicide!" he squeaked.

"The proof is in the doing," Duke said calmly.

"A cryptic message from the great beyond? You're losing it," the dragon gasped, growing smaller still. "Even if you're stupid enough to leap and I end up as tiny as a church mouse, I won't surrender—ever!"

It's funny, Duke thought. *I won this battle, yet I'm the one doing the surrendering.*

He took a deep breath and got into starting position. Maxine took her place beside him. Duke readied himself, rocking back and forth. Maxine readied herself, rocking back and forth.

Frantically the dragon tried to make himself disappear in an attempt to make a dignified exit, but he couldn't. "Drat! This is embarrassing!" he uttered in a tiny voice. Flustered, he scurried off, muttering angry somethings.

"Hey Maxine, my heart just got lighter!" Duke marveled.

She nodded. "Good timing."

Still rocking, Duke asked, "Do you think the universe would understand if I cross my fingers?"

"The universe understands everything," Maxine answered.

"Okay then, here we go!" he shouted, breaking into a sprint and charging toward the edge of the cliff.

Maxine hopped so fast to keep up that she became airborne. A moment later so did Duke. As his feet left the ground and he catapulted himself into the air, he let go of all that he could not control and took charge of all that he could.

Through the air the dragon slayer flew, his heart pounding with excitement and his eyes riveted on the bridge ahead. He felt weightless and free as the cool air rushed past his face. Maxine flew far above him so as not to disrupt his view—or his experience.

He began to level off and then started losing altitude—far short of the bridge.

"Hey Universe!" Duke called out, trying not to panic, "I've done *my* part. This might be a really good time for *you* to jump in. Uh, not into the river of course. That wasn't a joke. I'm dead serious. Well, not dead dead—at least not yet—but I really *am* in trouble here."

Despite his pleas he fell lower and lower, plummeting closer and closer to the raging river.

"Universe! Universe! If this is the right time to help me, please do it fast, before I find myself babbling to the fish!"

Dropping faster now, he waved his arms, trying to steer himself away from the rocks.

"THIS IS YOUR LAST CHANCE!" he yelled, shutting his eyes tight and sucking in his breath.

At the last possible moment a powerful gust of wind scooped him up, up out of the depths and whisked him onto the Bridge of Change.

CHAPTER EIGHTEEN

The Bridge of Change

Maxine swooped onto the bridge just as the Winds of Change set Duke down upon it.

"Whew, that was close!" he said, still shaken by the last-minute rescue. He took a deep, calming breath and then another, and checked to see if his satchel had survived the leap. It had. He smiled at Maxine. "How's that for taking action?"

"Very impressive. You and the universe are quite a team," Maxine remarked.

Suddenly melodious banjo music rang out above the sound of the rushing river and the whisper of the wind.

"Doc!" Duke said, turning to see the Wise One, hat and all, perched on the side of the bridge, grinning and strumming. "I'm so glad to see you! So much has happened!"

"Yes, I know," Doc answered, and he began to sing:

The Winds of Change answered your call.
Your faith has been rewarded.
They lifted you from troubled waters
And gently set you down.
Yea, the bridge—

"Yes, I made it! I really made it!" Duke blurted out, overcome with glee. "Oh, sorry for interrupting—hey, that song doesn't rhyme."

"I am trying out a new style," Doc said, still strumming.

"Why? I thought you loved rhyming."

"I do. I may also love not rhyming. Change can be as refreshing as it is inevitable."

Maxine chirped in approval. "He likes to stay in tune with the universe—forever changing."

Duke stood tall. "I'm getting in tune with the universe too. *I'm* forever changing."

"We all are," she said, fluffing her feathers. "We're wonderful works in progress."

"Yeah, I've been working hard to make some progress," Duke mused, staring back across the Leap of Faith. "Whoa, look at that! The fog's gone and the leap doesn't look that big from this side."

Doc nodded. "Yes, isn't that interesting. It seldom looks as big after you have taken it."

"I hope I'll feel the same way about the bridge after I cross it." He looked ahead into the distance. "There's still a lot of that—that Fog of Uncertainty out there, though."

"That's understandable. Change is full of uncertainty."

"I guess that's its nature," Duke said, his thoughts drifting to the stone in his satchel. "There's a certain amount of certainty in the uncertainty, isn't there?"

"Yes," Doc replied, "and it is that unknown that makes life a great adventure. Embrace the mystery, Duke, or the excitement of it will slip right through your fingers."

Maxine started bobbing up and down with enthusiasm. "Yes! Yes! That's what I've been saying. And guess what? Your last hero tool is for that exact purpose!"

Duke tried to think what was in his bag that he hadn't

used. Then he remembered. The mittens. He pulled them out and looked at them for the first time.

"I get it!" he exclaimed. "I wondered why there were mittens in here instead of heavy gloves fit for a dragon slayer."

He slid a mitten onto one hand and held it up. "Nothing could slip through your fingers with these on."

Then the whole idea struck him as so absurd that he began to laugh. That set off Maxine, who laughed and chirped and laughed some more.

Doc smiled and continued strumming. When the merry duo settled down, he sang:

> *The Winds of Change will guide you now*
> *From what is to what will be.*
> *Step by step you'll find your way*
> *Through the Fog of Uncertainty.*
>
> *Yea, the bridge over troubled waters*
> *It will take you home.*
> *And faith will sustain you*
> *Wherever you may roam.*

"You're rhyming again? What happened to change being refreshing?" Duke teased.

Doc shrugged his wings. "That is the way the lyrics came to me. Best to be flexible, to go with the flow." He looked at Maxine, who nodded in return. Together they sang the final chorus in perfect harmony:

> *Yea, the bridge over troubled waters*
> *It will take you home.*
> *Yea, the bridge will take you home.*

Duke applauded. "Great! Bravo!"

Maxine hopped into the air and flew a somersault, chirping. "Did you hear? It will take you home, Duke! *Home!* Get it?"

Duke was startled. "*Home?* You mean right now? I knew it would take me home eventually, but—but I can't go back yet! What about my heart?" He turned to Doc. "Doc, you told me that as I learn and live by the laws of the lands, serenity would replace the heaviness in my heart. You said it would grow lighter and lighter until finally I was set free. You *promised.*"

The owl waved his wing to quiet Duke down. "Not to worry," he assured him. "Serenity *has* been replacing the heaviness in your heart. Remember how you used to get so upset that all you could do was pace back and forth and crack your knuckles? Remember how much difficulty your best thinking got you into? And how you sighed with hopelessness, and how helpless you felt about your life running amok? And what about the churning in your stomach and the tightening of your throat and a mind stuffed so full of troubles that you kept bumping yourself and dropping things and forgetting where you put things?"

"I remember," Duke replied, recalling how bad things had once been. "And I had to lean back whenever I stood up or sat down so I wouldn't topple over, and I could hardly drag myself up a few stairs, like at the schoolhouse."

"Sometimes change happens gradually. One has to look back at what things were like before in order to appreciate how far one has come. You have come a long way, Duke."

"I know. And I know I'm still a work in progress. It's just that I was counting on being all peaceful and lighthearted before I had to face everyone back at home."

"The truth is that you cannot be all peaceful and lighthearted *until* you face everyone back at home," Doc corrected.

"To fully live by the laws of the lands, you need to implement them in your life. That means going home and using them to deal with the problems that drove you onto the Path of Serenity.

"Think of it this way. You have been using the laws to heal yourself. The next phase of your treatment is to use them to heal your life. You have done as much as you can here."

"Is that what you meant when you told me that all my most perplexing and troublesome problems would be solved? That I would learn how to solve them myself?"

"Yes, although your most troublesome problem, which I alluded to when first we met, has already been solved for the most part."

"It has? What was it?"

"Yourself. You were your biggest problem. The same is true of a vast majority of my patients. Of course most of them are not aware of it any more than you were. They start out believing the things that have happened to them are completely to blame for all their misery."

Duke shook his head. "Like those poor Bleaksvillites. Some of them know better and still don't do anything to help themselves."

"That's right," Maxine concurred. "You could have stayed with them, awfulizing and terribilizing your life away, but you didn't. You went where only the bravest dare to tread—back onto the Path of Serenity."

"Do you know what's amazing?" Duke said, reflecting. "Nothing has changed, but everything has changed. Everything that was wrong in my life still is, but now it all feels so ... different."

Doc looked deep into Duke's eyes. "It feels different because you are different in many respects and you are seeing it all differently."

"Yeah. That is *some* lesson about taking a different view of things and acting on it. When Willie first taught me about it I had no idea how powerful it would be."

A look of longing crept across Duke's face. "There is one thing I wish could be the way it used to be, though. I wish I could still be as fast as a bolt of lightning, as powerful as a tornado, and able to slay my prey with a single thrust of my sword."

"You never know what you might be able to achieve when you live by the laws of the lands," Doc said.

Duke took a deep breath. "So I need to take my calmer, more peaceful, wiser self back home to find lasting serenity and true lightheartedness," he reasoned, fully accepting the truth of the situation.

"A wise conclusion," Doc agreed. He stretched to his full height and flapped his wings twice. "Now let us celebrate your great victories. You have confronted and challenged the Dragon of Crooked Thinking, and you have both him and your Type II heart dis-ease on the run. That took great courage and skill. You have learned the laws of the lands and are mastering the secret of living by them. The hardest part is behind you.

"Hold your head high, Duke the Dragon Slayer. You have done yourself proud."

CHAPTER NINETEEN

Going Home

Noticing a familiar bird approaching, Doc began to play a cha-cha on his banjo. The bird glided down and landed beside Duke.

"Sebastian!" Duke cried out happily. "*Hola! Hola!* You found me again!"

Inspired by Doc's musical accompaniment, Sebastian delivered his most lively dance performance ever. Duke would have enjoyed it a lot more had he not been so apprehensive about reading the message the pigeon had brought with him this time.

After receiving accolades from his audience of three, Sebastian stood still while Duke removed two rolled notes from around his leg. "I trust you've brought better news this time," Duke said. "If not, I'm going to think twice about saying *gracias*." He paused for effect. Then he patted the pigeon on the head. "Just kidding."

Sebastian must have figured that anyone who could joke at a time like this deserved something special, so he did an encore before taking his leave. As he flew off, Duke called after him, "*Gracias, mi amigo*, for the delivery and for the extra dance."

Duke looked at Doc and Maxine for a clue as to what was in store for him, but they were silent. He stared down at the rolled messages in his hand. Closing his eyes, he took a deep, calming breath. Then he reached for the O Well water and took a sip, just in case. Nervously he unrolled the first note and read it aloud.

From the desk of . . .

WILLIE BURGUNDY
PROFESSOR AT-LARGE

Dear Duke,

Glad to hear you've whittled away your crooked thinking and are going home to carve out the new life you want. Finally being able to act on your new straight thoughts will make a world of difference in the way you think and feel.

You were an excellent student. If anyone can use the secret to turn his life around, as many have, it's you. Whatever happens, you'll be okay as long as you don't give anyone or anything the power to make you miserable.

Just keep thinking about your thinking, even about the small things that come up. Remember, your view is everything, and you—and your life— are what you say to yourself all day, every day.

Fondly,
Willie

Duke was both relieved and delighted. "One down and one to go," he said.

He took another deep, calming breath and hurriedly unrolled the second note.

Supreme Court
of
The Land of Serenity

To: Duke the Dragon Slayer

From: The Honorable Merlin the Magician

Heartfelt congratulations as you celebrate this momentous occasion.

My going-home gift to you is a bit of wisdom that has proven invaluable to many travelers like yourself. Learn these words and live by them, as you are living by the laws of the lands, for they, too, are an important part of lasting serenity and lightheartedness:

> *Live one day at a time, enjoy one*
> *moment at a time, and accept hardship*
> *as the pathway to peace.*

My entire entourage of furry friends, including our big, burly bailiff, join me in wishing you all the best as you carry on your never-ending fight for truth, proof, and the hero's way.

Brimming with happiness, Duke held up the notes. "This is a great sendoff!" he exclaimed.

"Yes, and that's not all," Maxine said, trying unsuccessfully to hide her excitement. "Can we give it to him now, Doc?"

Duke's eyes widened. "Give me what?"

"This," Doc answered, reaching into his black bag and holding up a small, shiny gold box with a large silver bow on top.

"That's for me?" Duke said, reaching for the box.

"It's your going-home gift from Doc and me," Maxine gushed. "Open it, Duke. I can't wait. You're going to love it!"

Duke was as excited as a child opening a birthday present. He lifted the lid and peeked inside. There, on a mound of cotton, was a sparkling gold medallion on a long gold chain. Speechless, he carefully lifted the chain out of the box and cradled the medallion gently in one hand, examining the tiny words engraved on it. He read them aloud:

> *Grant me the*
> SERENITY
> *to accept the things I cannot change,*
> COURAGE
> *to change the things I can, and*
> WISDOM
> *to know the difference.*

"Oh, you put all my little prayers together into one big one! I'll treasure this forever!" he said, unable to pull his eyes away from the words.

Maxine was jumping with joy. "Isn't that great? Now turn it over!" She giggled. "I mean the medallion, of course."

Smiling, Duke eagerly looked on the back. Sure enough, it too was engraved. He read:

> *Live one day at a time,*
> *enjoy one moment at a time, and*
> *accept hardship as the pathway to peace.*

"Merlin's words of wisdom! How can I ever thank you two enough?"

In a sage voice Doc replied, "Our thanks will be your commitment to living by the laws of the lands and the wise words in Merlin's note, and using the prayer to ask for help when you need it."

Duke nodded. "I will. I promise." He put the chain over his head and around his neck. The medallion came to rest over his heart.

Suddenly little wisps of wind swirled up and gently nudged Duke forward. "Hey," he said. "What's happening?"

"The winds have decided it's time for you to go," Maxine explained.

Anxious as Duke was to get back home and straighten out his life, the thought of leaving his newfound friends saddened him.

"Is there any chance Maxine could cross the bridge with me, even partway?" he asked.

"She has brought you as far as she can," Doc said. "The rest is up to you."

"What if I have more questions?"

"I'll tell him," Maxine said eagerly. "You can always ask yourself what Doc would say, or Willie, or Merlin, or I."

He set down his satchel and turned to her. "Would you sit on my shoulder one last time?"

She promptly flew over and nestled her feathery head against his neck. "I'm going to miss you too," she whispered, her voice cracking with emotion.

He stroked her gently. A tear rolled down his cheek. "You really are a Bluebird of Happiness, Maxine, and creating happiness really is your greatest gift. Thanks for everything. I'll never forget you."

She chirped and stepped off his shoulder, fluttered her wings hummingbird style, and gracefully lowered herself back onto the bridge.

Duke turned to Doc. "I'll always be grateful to the universe for sending you to me, and to you and your friends for teaching me how to lighten my heart, O Wise One, Henry Herbert Hoot, D.H. May I shake your hand—uh, wing?"

"It would be an honor," Doc said grandly, extending his wing. "Your life begins anew today, Duke the Dragon Slayer."

"Today—and every day, I guess," Duke replied, shaking Doc's wing. He picked up his satchel. "Well, here goes. Neither fog nor winds nor swaying of the bridge will deter me from completing my mission."

He took a few steps, then paused and turned back to wave a final good-bye. What he saw made him burst out in laughter. Maxine was spinning around and around in a blur like a toy top.

"What are you doing, Maxine?" he called out.

Her voice came in short bursts. "These trips...tend to be ...somewhat stressful...not to mention...the good-byes.... This is how...I unwind."

"You're always full of surprises."

"Yes...like change and life....Isn't it...fun!"

"I hope it will be—eventually," Duke said uneasily. He turned toward home again, only to see the Fog of Uncertainty closing in around him. In a flash he thought about his thinking and thrust his hand out in front of him. "STOP!" he ordered. "People cross this bridge all the time. I can make it!"

He took a deep, calming breath. Immediately his straight-thinking stick and New View glasses and O Well water and stone and tape measure and mittens and book of lessons for the heart seemed to march into his head and fan out like little soldiers on a search-and-destroy mission.

A moment later the fog began to lift and his heart grew lighter still.

"Whoa, these hero tools are really something!" he remarked. "Hey, my satchel! It's gone!"

He glanced down to see if he had dropped it. To his amazement, he found himself standing on a cobblestone road.

"What—what's going on here?" he gasped, looking back

to see if the bridge was still behind him. But it too was gone—and so were the river and the cliff and Doc and Maxine.

"What's happening?" he muttered. "How could everything just disappear?"

His mind raced with possibilities. Maybe this and maybe that. Maybe Doc and Maxine had outdone themselves with their magical powers, or maybe none of it was real and his mind was running more amok than his life ever had. He stood frozen in time and space, not knowing what to think or what to do.

Slowly he became aware of a tingly, comforting warmth in the center of his chest. It radiated up and down and out and around until his entire body had filled with its presence. He looked down at his chest. There, resting over his heart, was the gold medallion. It was glowing. He reached up and clutched it in his hand.

Rays of sunlight shone brightly through the scattered patches of remaining fog and danced upon the cobblestone road that seemed to be beckoning him home. *Home*, he thought. *I'm really going home. Home to turn my life around.*

A tower of hope and determination, Duke read once again the words etched into his precious medallion and repeated the prayer that would carry him the rest of the way to lasting serenity and lightheartedness.

Grant me the
SERENITY
to accept the things I cannot change,
COURAGE
to change the things I can, and
WISDOM
to know the difference.

He closed his eyes tightly and pressed the medallion to his chest. "Okay, Universe, I'll do my part. And I know you'll do yours."

Duke couldn't remember the last time his heart had felt so light. He actually was happy—even though he still really, REALLY wished some things were different.

With the brisk stride of a man on a mission, he continued on, chanting, "Grant me serenity, courage, and wisdom . . . serenity, courage, and wisdom . . ."

All of a sudden he heard the faint sound of a dog barking somewhere in the distance. As it came closer it sounded more and more familiar. *Could it possibly be?* he wondered, his heart beating faster.

A moment later he knew.

"Prince! Prince!" he shouted, breaking into a run. "I'm coming, boy! Everything's going to be all right!

"I'm coming home."

The Beginning

May the road rise to meet you,
  may the wind be always at your back,
 may the sun shine warm upon your face
   and the rain fall soft upon your fields,
 and until we meet again, dear reader . . .
   may God hold you in the hollow of His hand.

I invite you to meet an extraordinary princess and accompany her on an enlightening journey. You will laugh with her and cry with her, learn with her and grow with her . . . and she will become a dear friend you will never forget.

Marcia Grad Powers

1 MILLION COPIES SOLD WORLDWIDE

The Princess Who Believed in Fairy Tales

"Here is a very special book that will guide you lovingly into a new way of thinking about yourself and your life so that the future will be filled with hope and love and song."

OG MANDINO
Author, *The Greatest Salesman in the World*

The Princess Who Believed in Fairy Tales by Marcia Grad is a personal growth book of the rarest kind. It's a delightful, humor-filled story you will experience so deeply that it can literally change your feelings about yourself, your relationships, and your life.

The princess's journey of self-discovery on the Path of Truth is an eye-opening, inspiring, empowering psychological and spiritual journey that symbolizes the one we all take through life as we separate illusion from reality, come to terms with our childhood dreams and pain, and discover who we really are and how life works.

If you have struggled with childhood pain, with feelings of not being good enough, with the loss of your dreams, or if you have been disappointed in your relationships, this book will prove to you that happy endings—and new beginnings—are always possible. Or, if you simply wish to get closer to your own truth, the princess will guide you.

The universal appeal of this book has resulted in its translation into numerous languages.

Excerpts from Readers' Heartfelt Letters

"*The Princess* is truly a gem! Though I've read a zillion self-help and spiritual books, I got more out of this one than from any other one I've ever read. It is just too illuminating and full of wisdom to ever be able to thank you enough. The friends and family I've given copies to have raved about it."

"*The Princess* is powerful, insightful, and beautifully written. I am seventy years old and have seldom encountered greater wisdom. I've been waiting to read this book my entire life. You are a psychologist, a guru, a saint, and an angel all wrapped up into one. I thank you with all my heart."

Available wherever books are sold or send $15.00 (CA res. $16.39) plus $3.00 S/H to Wilshire Book Co., 7531 Variel Avenue, Chatsworth, CA 91311.

For our complete catalog, visit our Web site at www.mpowers.com.

The Magic of Getting What You Want

Here is the book that could well become your blueprint for personal fulfillment. It was written by one of the foremost authorities on motivation, the author of that enormously successful book *The Magic of Thinking Success*, which has sold more than one million copies.

Now, in this immensely readable, practical, and comforting volume, Dr. Schwartz tells us how we can have more wealth, influence, and happiness by approaching life positively and planning our goals creatively. Dr. Schwartz emphasizes that, after analyzing our special assets and capabilities and deciding what we should do with them, we must also be willing to make certain personal adjustments to get what we want.

Although most of us know what we should be doing with our lives, we need to be reminded of the many ways in which others have achieved their goals. This down-to-earth book is a veritable treasury of inspiration and practical suggestions for everyone who wants to develop a winning philosophy—and, as Dr. Schwartz believes, "a winning philosophy always produces winners."

Find out how to

- Turn your dreams into attainable goals
- Make your mental vision work for you
- Feel confident in any business or social situation
- Win others to your way of thinking

The way you lived yesterday determined your today. But the way you live today will determine your tomorrow. Every day is a new opportunity to become the way you want to be and to have your life become what you want it to be.

Take the first step toward becoming all you're capable of being. Read *The Magic of Getting What You Want* and follow the proven step-by-step plan that can help anyone develop the ultimate in personal power. Then get ready for an incredible adventure that will change you and your life forever.

If you feel as though you are on a runaway emotional roller coaster with your partner at the controls, this book is for you! It can save you years of torment, tumult, and tears.

The Powerful, Life-Changing Secret of Overcoming Verbal Abuse

If you are being mistreated by your partner, *The Secret of Overcoming Verbal Abuse* can dramatically change your life. You will learn an entirely new way of perceiving and coping with your relationship and your feelings.

The time-tested, proven secret contained in this book will wrap itself around you like a thick, warm, protective blanket, insulating you from your pain. And the next time your "Prince Charming" takes aim and tries to pierce your heart with his unkind words, you will be ready. You will feel strong and be in charge of your own reaction.

Whether you want to stay, need to stay, or plan to leave, this book can help you to

- Set yourself free from confusion, anxiety, frustration, self-doubt, guilt, anger, and depression
- Restore your dignity, self-respect, self-love, and personal power
- Create the inner peace and happiness you have wanted, wished for, and in tearful, private moments prayed for—perhaps for years

Get ready to begin an exciting journey of enlightenment and empowerment that will help you regain control of your life. Your guides will be **Dr. Albert Ellis**, one of the most famous and influential psychologists in the world, and **Marcia Grad Powers**, accredited Rational Emotive Behavior Therapy (REBT) educator and bestselling author.

Books by Albert Ellis, Ph.D.

A GUIDE TO RATIONAL LIVING
1.5 Million Copies Sold

1. How Far Can You Go with Self-Therapy? 2. You Largely Feel the Way You Think 3. Feeling Well by Thinking Straight 4. How You Create Your Feelings 5. Thinking Yourself Out of Emotional Disturbances 6. Recognizing and Reducing Neurotic Behavior 7. Overcoming the Influences of the Past 8. Is Reason Always Reasonable? 9. Refusing to Feel Desperately Unhappy 10. Tackling Your Dire Need for Approval 11. Reducing Your Dire Fears of Failure 12. How to Start Blaming and Start Living 13. How to Feel Frustrated but Not Depressed or Enraged 14. Controlling Your Own Emotional Destiny 15. Conquering Anxiety and Panic 16. Acquiring Self-Discipline 17. Rewriting Your Personal History 18. Accepting and Coping with the Grim Facts of Life 19. Overcoming Inertia and Getting Creatively Absorbed 304 Pages . . . $15.00

A GUIDE TO PERSONAL HAPPINESS

1. Why Search for Personal Happiness? 2. ABC's of Personal Happiness 3. Main Blocks to Personal Happiness 4. Disputing and Uprooting Emotional Disturbance 5. Emotive Methods of Achieving Personal Happiness 6. Behavioral Methods of Achieving Personal Happiness 7. Ten Rules for Achieving Personal Happiness 8. Overcoming Shyness and Feelings of Inadequacy 9. Overcoming Feelings of Guilt 10. Coping with Depression and Low Frustration Tolerance 11. Coping with Anger and with Mating Problems 12. Overcoming Sex Problems 13. Coping with Work Problems 14. Summing Up: Eliminating Your Self-Created Roadblocks to Personal Happiness 15. Upward and Onward to Self-Actualizing and Joy 144 Pages . . . $10.00

HOW TO LIVE WITH A NEUROTIC

1. The Possibility of Helping Troubled People 2. How to Recognize a Person with Emotional Disturbance 3. How Emotional Disturbances Originate 4. Some Basic Factors in Emotional Upsets 5. How to Help a Neurotic Overcome Disturbance 6. How to Live with a Person Who Remains Neurotic 7. How to Live with Yourself Though You Fail to Help a Neurotic 160 Pages . . . $10.00

HOW TO RAISE AN EMOTIONALLY HEALTHY, HAPPY CHILD

1. Neurotics Are Born as Well as Made 2. What Is a Neurotic Child? 3. Helping Children Overcome Fears and Anxieties 4. Helping Children with Problems of Achievement 5. Helping Children Overcome Hostility 6. Helping Children Become Self-Disciplined 7. Helping Children with Sex Problems 8. Helping Children with Conduct Problems 9. Helping Children with Personal Behavior Problems 10. How to Live with a Neurotic Child and Like It 256 Pages . . . $10.00

A GUIDE TO SUCCESSFUL MARRIAGE

1. Modern Marriage: Hotbed of Neurosis 2. Factors Causing Marital Disturbance 3. Gauging Marital Compatibility 4. Problem Solving in Marriage 5. Can We Be Intelligent About Marriage? 6. Love or Infatuation? 7. To Marry or Not to Marry 8. Sexual Preparation for Marriage 9. Impotence in the Male 10. Frigidity in the Female 11. Sex Excess 12. Controlling Sex Impulses 13. Non-monogamous Desires 14. Communication in Marriage 15. Children 16. In-Laws 17. Marital Incompatibility Versus Neurosis 18. Divorce 19. Succeeding in Marriage 304 Pages . . . $10.00